THE STARS FOR SAM

By the same author

THE EARTH FOR SAM

WHITE STREAMERS AND RED FLAMES

Figure 1. The combination of the brilliant white light of the sun and the dazzling reflection of daylight in our air prevents us from seeing the beautiful corona and the crimson flames. Probably many of the stars are surrounded by corona streamers and colored flames. In addition some of the stars are basically green, blue, or red. To a stellar Marco Polo a near view of our Milky Way must surpass all dreams of oriental splendor. (From a photograph of the sun taken by the Mt. Wilson Observatory staff at Green River, Wyoming, during an eclipse of the sun on June 18, 1918. Colored by Mrs. Alice H. Park under the direction of Alfred H. Joy. Courtesy of the Mt. Wilson Observatory.)

THE STARS
FOR SAM

BY W. MAXWELL REED

Edited by Charles E. St. John

Decorations by Karl Moseley

HARCOURT, BRACE AND COMPANY

NEW YORK

PREFACE

THE young people of today are learning about an entirely different universe from the so-called "classical" science of the days when the author went to school. The new conceptions will appear as commonplace to the coming generation as they are incredible to those of the author's generation. It has been therefore the main object of this book to start the boy and girl of today with a fair comprehension of the new conceptions of space, time, and matter. Over and over again, and from different points of view, the author has endeavored to make some of these marvelous discoveries clear. Also an effort has been made to show the relationship of one branch of physics to another, and how one law, used as a tool, can be made to formulate grand laws of primary importance.

No effort has been made to make this book a compilation of facts. On the contrary, every effort has been made to show the uncertainty of our knowledge. When the author went to school he had the impression that his teachers and the libraries together represented almost complete knowledge. He appreciated that there were some things still to be discovered, but not many. Now he finds himself trying to impart to the next generation exactly the opposite doctrine. He wants to make clear not only

PREFACE

that we are on the verge of making great discoveries as yet unsuspected, but that due to our limitations in the three dimensional world we can probably never really understand the space-time-life world. Our three dimensional minds must ever have distorted ideas. Harry Kemp in his poem "Blind" (*Chanteys and Ballads,* published by Brentano's, Inc.) has given this idea both beautifully and concisely:

> The Spring blew trumpets of colour;
> Her green sang in my brain;
> I heard a blind man groping
> *Tap-tap* with his cane.
> I pitied him his blindness;
> But can I boast I see?
>
> Perhaps there lurks a spirit
> Nearby, who pities me—
> A spirit who sees me tapping
> My five-sensed cane of mind
> Amid such unguessed glories
> That I am worse than blind!

The author wishes to acknowledge his indebtedness to his wife, to his sister, Mrs. Douglas S. Studdiford and to Mr. Forest A. Irwin, principal of the Nishuane School, Montclair, N. J. The author is especially grateful for the very careful editing by Dr. Charles E. St. John, of the Mt. Wilson Observatory.

W. MAXWELL REED.

Old Greenwich, Connecticut,
July 16, 1931.

CONTENTS

CONTENTS

A CALIFORNIA OBSERVATORY

Figure 2. The Lick Observatory of the University of California on Mount Hamilton. (Courtesy of the Lick Observatory.)

I: THE SUN

HE sun must have been the first heavenly body to attract attention at the very dawn of intelligence in the animal kingdom. It was the mysterious giver of light and heat, and mysterious it still is. It is beyond our power to imagine what the heat of the sun and its dazzling brilliancy would be if we were near it. We know that the temperature of the surface of the sun is about 11,000° Fahrenheit, but the center of the sun is estimated to be 70 million degrees Fahrenheit. Such figures mean very little to any of us. All we can say is that the sun is so hot that it would be dangerous to get much nearer to it than we are at present.

That the sun is round was probably one of the first astronomical discoveries ever made. You can make that discovery yourself by looking at the sun at sunset on any clear day. It will appear as a red ball.

In early ages, men believed that the sun rose in the east and set in the west, and we still speak of it as doing just that. We know now, however, that it does nothing of the sort. The sun really stands still, and all the motion belongs to the earth, which is spinning around it. Copernicus of Poland was the first modern astronomer to discover that the earth revolves around the sun.

The sun was absolutely perfect to our ancestors who lived in Europe during the Dark Ages, which followed the fall of Rome. It is easy to see why they regarded it as a brilliant sphere without a flaw. Whether we look at the setting sun seen through the dust-laden air, or by means of smoked glass at the dazzling light of the noonday sun, we almost always see a flawless disc. Apparently it has clean-cut edges and is as smooth as a lens. Imagine Galileo's surprise when he looked at the sun for the first time through a telescope, and found several black spots on its surface (Figure 3).

This discovery made Galileo very unpopular. He had destroyed an ideal. It was as bad as criticizing a hero. Nowadays, we want to find out all we can about the sun, and the more we discover, the more wonderful that source of light appears to be.

Through a large telescope the surface of the sun looks like a mass of clouds, each of which is at least one hundred, and sometimes several hundred, miles across. These are not clouds of rain or snow but masses of incandescent vapor where gases of iron, lead, tin, and other substances are rising from the caldron.

These apparent clouds are not real clouds of condensed vapors like the clouds in our atmosphere. From cool and quiet observatories on the earth we look across a space of over ninety million

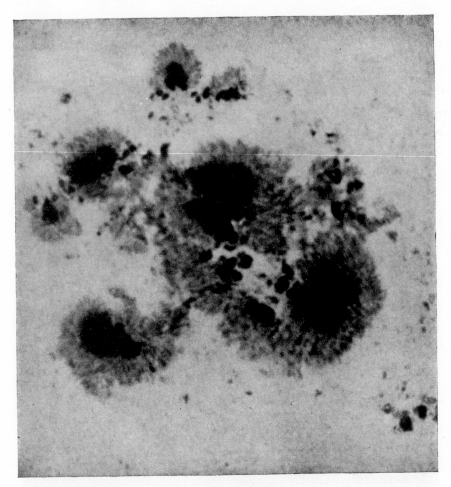

A GREAT SUN-SPOT

Figure 3. These black spots look like holes in a sea of clouds. They are not holes. We are looking down upon storm centers, which are of giant size; for that black disc in the lower left-hand corner represents the earth. In violence too these storms are worse than the hurricanes which come to Florida and Texas from the West Indies. From the turbulent neighborhood of these spots, the red flames rise with explosive violence. The fleecy white clouds have a temperature of about 11,000° Fahrenheit, but the rising and twisting gases which give the appearance of black spots are only about 7,500° Fahrenheit. (From a photograph taken at the Mt. Wilson Observatory, August 8, 1917. Courtesy of the Mt. Wilson Observatory.)

PARIS SEES AN ECLIPSE OF THE SUN

Figure 4. "On April 17, 1912, this point of the cone swept the neighborhood of Paris at ten minutes past noon." (Drawn by Lucien Rudaux for article by G. F. Chambers in *Marvels of the Universe*. Courtesy of Hutchinson & Co., Ltd., London.)

miles and into a blazing furnace. Innumerable masses of gas and flame are rising and falling. Explosions, greater than any volcanic outburst, are taking place continually. As we look into this primeval mass we see an apparent surface of mottled clouds like a "mackerel" sky on the earth. Could we fly there, we would find there were no clouds at all, but merely masses of gas of different temperatures, some expanding and rising, others contracting and falling. At our enormous distance they look like a smooth sea of fleecy clouds. To a salamander in an asbestos airplane there would be no clear-cut surface to this sea of fire. As he flew from the sun's interior he would be conscious of passing through gases of different degrees of heat, even of different substances. Gradually the superheated atmosphere would become rarefied and cooler. When the salamander was well on his way home, if he should look back he would see a sharply defined sun with a surface of closely packed, fleecy incandescent clouds. Then he would tell his associates that what they called the surface of the sun was, to some extent, an optical illusion.

"Do not get close to those dark spots," he would probably warn them, "for they are like the 'twisters' in the Mississippi Valley. They are tornadoes in the fiery vapor. Also beware of those huge spouting flames which are many times larger than this earth. They move faster than a cannon-ball and might destroy everything within their reach."

Those innocent black spots which Galileo saw for the first

3

time are veritable volcanoes. Great masses of gas rise from the sun's interior, twisting, as they rise, like waterspouts and tornadoes. Then they flow out over that part of the sun which looks to us like a surface. As they rush up from the interior and overflow in all directions, they never rise more than about five hundred miles from the imaginary surface of the sun called the photosphere (sphere of light).

We look down upon those columns of gas from the top. They rise so rapidly that they have cooled to some extent. In contrast to those illusive layers of incandescent clouds they look actually black; yet compared with white-hot molten iron these "black" spots are intensely bright.

To illustrate how brilliant a sun-spot really is, the dazzling stream of white-hot iron as it was poured from a furnace was compared with a sun-spot. This was done by arranging mirrors in such a way that when you looked through the telescope you saw the stream of iron alongside the sun-spot. To every one's surprise, the stream of molten iron looked darker than the sun-spot. It was "blacker" than Galileo's "black" spots. Now we can get some idea of the intense brilliance of those fleeting and imaginary clouds of incandescent gas.

The black spot, as we have said, is something like the crater of a volcano. Of course it is a temporary crater. Since it has no hard sides and permanent place, it is more like a tornado in our air. The cooler gas spreads out in all directions, not so much

AS THE ECLIPSE APPEARED IN ALL AGES

Figure 5. From a photograph of the total eclipse of the sun on January 24, 1925, taken in the Bronx Park, New York City. (Copyrighted by A. Fassbender, Amervoll Company, 1170 Broadway, New York City.)

CORONA

Figure 6. That black disc is the moon, which is temporarily shielding us from the blinding light of the sun. Under such circumstances we can see the marvelous shafts of white light which are radiated from the sun in all directions. From the two poles small streamers radiate like "northern lights" (aurora borealis). The size of this display can be realized when you recall that the diameter of the sun is nearly a million miles; consequently these streamers are nearly half a million miles long. (From a photograph taken by the eclipse expedition of the Lick Observatory at Padang, Sumatra, on May 18, 1901. Courtesy of the Lick Observatory.)

like lava as like water spouting up from a hole in the bottom of a basin and overflowing. The gas spreads over the imaginary surface, the photosphere. If you look at a picture of a tornado, you will see that the dust- and water-laden air spreads out in large flat clouds when it reaches a certain height above the surface of the earth. In other words, this rising, twisting air of the tornado flows out over an imaginary surface in the air when it rises to a certain height, and therefore behaves somewhat like the cooler gas rising in a twisting column in what we call a sun-spot.

The flowing of the sun-spot gas over the surface of the photosphere causes a very curious thing to take place. There is nothing on the earth which is exactly like this queer thing, and therefore it is a little difficult to understand. The intensely hot substances of which the sun is made give off such bright light that atoms which are free to move are driven away, for it is an interesting fact that light, like wind, has a force which can blow away extremely tiny particles. Even an ordinary candle flame has such a repelling power, but it is so feeble that you don't realize it. If, however, you were a tiny atom and if you were near that terrifically hot and brilliant sun, then you would feel the repelling force of light. In another chapter we shall find that this delicate force can, under certain circumstances, regulate the size of stars.

That outflowing layer of cooler gas which came from the

spouting sun-spot acts something like a screen for the intense sunlight. The atoms, hovering above this cooler layer of out-flowing gas, are not repelled upward so fast as the atoms which are to one side, and which therefore get the full force of the terrifically intense sunlight. This difference in the forces which are repelling these atoms causes a commotion. The atoms driven away by the intense light on all sides of the spot flow into this quieter space over the cooler gas surrounding a sun-spot. Again we have a twisting motion. The atoms and mole-cules, taking refuge behind this cooler gas as a screen, elbow each other until they are spinning around like a whirlpool.

This second whirlpool of hot, rotating gas is about 10,000 miles high. Thus the commotion, which the cooler gas from the sun-spot caused by cutting off a little of the intense sunlight, extends up into the atmosphere of the sun for thousands of miles.

So we have two whirlpools of gases for any well-developed sun-spot. Why the lower one should consist of uprushing gases from some invisible place in the sun we do not know.

These solar tornadoes last much longer than those on the earth. They usually are visible for many days and sometimes for months. It was by watching these long-enduring solar storms that we first discovered that the sun was turning on its axis like the earth. As you might expect from such a huge body, nearly a million miles in diameter, it turns much more slowly than the

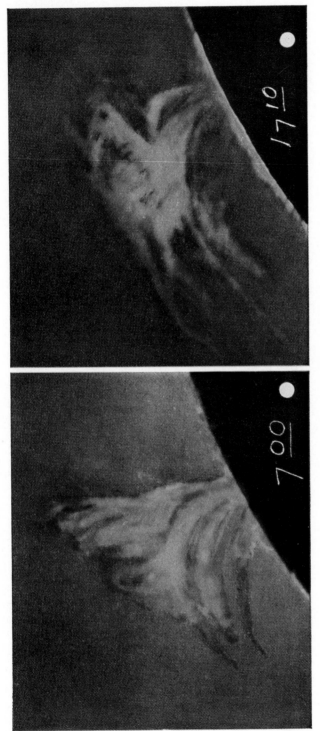

TEN HOURS AND TEN MINUTES IN THE LIFE OF A FLAME

Figures 7 and 8. What celestial wind is blowing this solar flame? That little white circle in the lower right-hand corner represents the size of the earth, which as you know is 8,000 miles in diameter. Obviously, then, in ten hours the flame moved many thousands of miles. Apparently it was blown aside with a speed which would have taken it from New York City to San Francisco in one hour. (From a photograph taken at the Mt. Wilson Observatory of a "quiescent" prominence 110,000 miles high, June 10, 1917, colored by Mrs. Alice Howard Park under the direction of Alfred H. Joy. Courtesy of the Mt. Wilson Observatory.)

earth, making one revolution in about 25 days. It twists on its axis in the same direction in which the earth goes around the sun. If that salamander wanted to cool off after his visit to the sun, he might have flown high into space toward the North Star. Then, if he had looked down upon the sun, moon, and earth, he would have seen the sun twisting on its axis counter-clockwise—turning in the opposite way from the hands of a clock. The earth would have been running around the sun, also counterclockwise, and at the same time spinning on its axis in the same direction. The salamander would notice that the moon was circling around the earth also counterclockwise. "This looks like a real law," the salamander would exclaim as he finally noticed that all the planets—Mercury, Venus, Mars, Jupiter, Saturn, Uranus, Neptune, and Pluto—travel around the sun, all counterclockwise.

Once in a while the moon, in its counterclockwise journey around the earth, comes directly between us and the sun (Figure 4). For a few seconds the sun is completely hidden—eclipsed. Then we can see what is happening on the edge of the sun. Ordinarily the sun is so dazzlingly bright that we cannot see its atmosphere. Also when the sun is setting in the west, the same dust which enables us to see it as a clearly defined round, red ball, prevents us from seeing its atmosphere. By this time we must suspect that this atmosphere is very brilliant even if we cannot see it.

THE SUN

During an eclipse, the blinding light of the sun is temporarily hidden behind the moon. Then we see the brilliant solar atmosphere. Huge red flames are seen to spout from the sun's surface (Figures 7, 8 and 9). They are the explosive flames which the salamander found associated with the solar tornadoes—the sunspots. They are enormously high—one hundred thousand miles, or more. Of course, they are appearing and disappearing and constantly changing their fantastic shapes. They always contain incandescent hydrogen, a gas which shines with red light at the high temperature of the sun (Figure 5).

In the illustration opposite can be seen, besides those giant red flames which are many hundreds of times larger than the earth, numerous smaller ones. They are dancing everywhere in the great mass of gas which surrounds the sun. By an ingenious device the astronomers of Mt. Wilson have taken a photograph of those innumerable red flames. They have taken it in such a way as to show red flames and nothing else. You would think from this picture that the sun is red. It is merely that by this clever device only the red flames were photographed and none of the other colors were allowed to come through to the photographic plate. It well illustrates the seething turmoil of the sun's atmosphere. One of those giant flames is just appearing over the distant sun's horizon. The sun is a terrible monster: to be too far away from it means death by freezing, to be too near means death by burning.

8

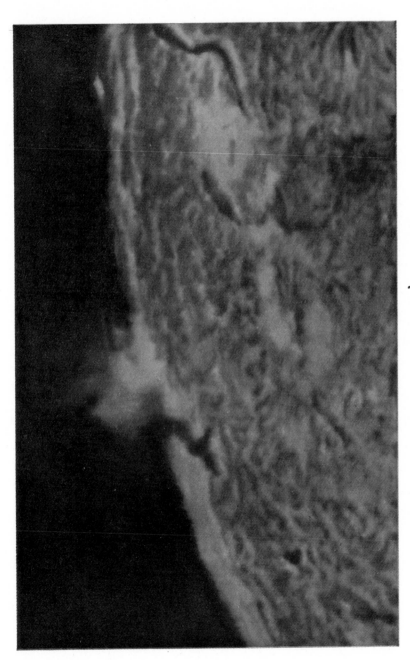

THE RED FLAMES IN THE SUN'S ATMOSPHERE

Figure 9. (From a photograph taken at the Mt. Wilson Observatory by means of the H line in the solar spectrum, June 30, 1917. The photograph was colored by Mrs. Alice Howard Park under the direction of Alfred H. Joy. Courtesy of the Mt. Wilson Observatory.)

Stretching far out beyond the sun, sometimes several million miles, is a white halo called the "corona" (Figures 1 and 6). It looks something like a glorified display of "northern lights." Just what it is we do not know. If it is a gas, it must be an excessively rarefied one—more nearly resembling our idea of a vacuum than a gas. Perhaps it is in part the illuminated portion of a great cloud of celestial particles. The arrangement of these particles may have been distorted by the magnetic attraction of the sun into long filaments, which, when illuminated, give the appearance we see in the photographs (Figures 1 and 6). In later chapters we will consider what such a celestial dust cloud would be like, and its possible effect upon our climate.

II: THE MILKY WAY

O N A clear night the sky is full of stars. There apparently are countless millions of them. If, however, you start to count those which are visible to the naked eye, you will be surprised how few there really are. Until the invention of the telescope no one, probably, saw more than two thousand stars at any one time. But with this wonderful invention many more than 1,000 million stars can be photographed.

Even through the telescope the stars, with few exceptions, are merely specks of light (Figure 10). They have no round disc like the sun as it disappears below the western horizon. They look through the telescope as they do to the naked eye, only very much brighter.

The few exceptions to this rule are interesting. 'Way back in prehistoric times people discovered that some stars wander and occupy different places in the sky. The ancients thought they were spirits moving around in the heavens. Through the telescope you can see that these "spirits" are globes like the earth and moon. We call them planets (wandering stars) and know

10

that they revolve around the sun as the earth does (Figure 11).

Mercury is the name of the planet that is nearest to the sun. Like most planets, it moves in a nearly circular path called its orbit.

Then as we go out from the sun we cross the nearly circular paths of Mercury, Venus, the earth, Mars, Jupiter, Saturn, Uranus, Neptune, and finally Pluto, the very outermost of the planets. Neptune and Pluto are so far away that they are visible only in a telescope. Yet it is not far when compared with the nearest star.

The other stars, the ones which seem innumerable, are called "fixed" stars. The planets are millions of miles from the sun and earth, but the fixed stars are vastly farther away. We know these stars are round, but even with the most powerful telescope we never can see their shape—they are always just brilliant points like distant electric lights.

For a couple of thousand stars we know the distances in miles because we have measured most of these distances as a surveyor would measure them.

It has been found that the nearest star is so far away that light from it, traveling 186,000 miles per second, takes four years to reach us. Yet under the most favorable conditions light from Neptune can reach the earth in less than four hours, and light from the sun reaches the earth in eight minutes.

It may seem strange that light takes time to travel. You probably thought that light flashed instantly in all directions. Nearly all your ancestors would agree with you, for it is only since 1675 that we have known that light takes time to travel through space, just as waves take time to travel across a pond. In some later chapter we will learn more about this curious subject.

We can measure very great distances in space by "light-years." A light-year is an imaginary measuring-rod so long that it would take light traveling at 186,000 miles per second one year to go from one end to the other. For example, it is about four light-years to the nearest fixed star. That Cloud of Magellan (Figure 10) is 100,000 light-years away.

The stars look as if they were fastened to an immense dome of some blue material. Apparently they are all the same distance away; only some are bigger than others. Also we notice a broad white path that nearly divides the heavens into two equal parts —we call it the Milky Way. The Egyptians thought it was a river over which the spirits of dead Pharaohs used to sail in their boats.

If the Egyptians had ever looked at the Milky Way through a telescope they never would have thought that it was a river (Figure 13). In a telescope that white light disappears, and we see nothing but myriads of individual stars.

This is another example of how deceptive appearances can be. It is very much like looking at a forest on the side of a distant mountain. From a long way off the forest appears to be a

THE SMALLER OF THE CLOUDS OF MAGELLAN

Figure 10. Like a little cloud which had blown away from the Milky Way, this mass of perhaps a million or more stars is visible to the naked eye near the South Pole. It is a faint patch of light about four times as long as the diameter of the moon. If all the light of all these stars were concentrated at one point we would find that point about as bright as the North Star. This faintness is due to the enormous distance. Some stars in this cloud are known to be two hundred thousand times brighter than our sun. If the sun suddenly acquired such brightness all life would be destroyed. (From a photograph taken at the Harvard College branch observatory at Arequipa, Peru, with the Bruce telescope, 2 feet in diameter, on November 10, 1898; exposure 5 hours. Courtesy of the Harvard College Observatory.)

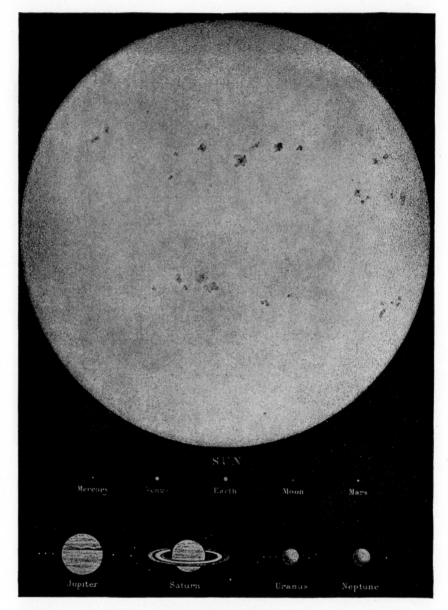

THE SOLAR FAMILY

Figure 11. When the whole solar system is drawn upon the same scale, the earth looks a little insignificant. As for the moon, she barely registers. Even those dark spots upon the sun are many times larger than that tiny white speck we call the earth. (*The Heavens,* by Amédée Guillemin; publisher, Richard Bentley, 1867. Pluto was not discovered when this diagram was made in 1867.)

smooth dark green band. Using a spy-glass you see the individual trees, which seem very close together. If you actually went
to the forest you might find the trees were wide apart so that
you could ride a horse among them.

That the stars are all the same distance from us is also only a
matter of appearance. Some are many thousands of times more
distant than others. Occasionally three stars will appear to be
close together and, perhaps, in a straight line. In reality, one
star may be immensely farther off than the other two. They just
happen to appear to us to be in a straight line and near together.
As you might suppose, generally speaking, the fainter stars are
farther away than the brighter ones. The bigger the telescope,
the more of these faint, far-distant stars we can see. As a rule the
stars are as far from each other as we are from them (Figure
14).

At first one might assume that the stars extended indefinitely
into space and that there was no limit to this forest of lights.
That is not true, for by a very ingenious method astronomers
have discovered that there is a limit. If you keep looking at one
place in the sky and use larger and larger telescopes, you will be
able to count more and more stars. Yet when you finally use
some very large telescopes, you will be disappointed in the number of new stars which you can count. If the stars were scattered
through space without limit, you would not expect this result.
You would assume quite properly that the bigger the telescope

you used, the more stars you would see. It seems, therefore, that when you use a very large telescope, you are looking out through the stars into the darkness of empty space.

EGYPTIAN CONSTELLATIONS

Figure 12. "Chart of the stars in the region of the north pole. The sky was considered the abode of the gods and certain mythical creatures, who were given definite places in the heavens, as here indicated by stars and circles on the figures." The photographs were taken by Harry Burton in the sepulchral chamber of the tomb of the Egyptian Pharaoh Seti I, XIX dynasty (about 1300 B.C.). This tomb is in the famous Valley of the Kings on the west bank of the Nile, opposite the ancient capital of Egypt, Thebes. The Great Dipper (Ursa Major) is represented by the bull and the figure of a man, with his head crowned by a disc, near the tail of the bull. He is holding what looks like two ropes proceeding from the base of the bull's tail. The four small circles on this man represent the bowl of the dipper. The two small circles on the bull perhaps represent the handle of the dipper. ("An Ancient Egyptian Astronomical Ceiling-Decoration," bulletin of the Metropolitan Museum of Art, 1923, L-7068-G, 56. Courtesy of the Metropolitan Museum of Art.)

Let us imagine a large city surrounded by an almost uninhabited country, and let us imagine that at night you go to the top of a tower near the center of that city. You will see a few hundred street lights around you; the rest are lost in the haze. You take a small spy-glass so that you can see the lights for a

THE MILKY WAY

Figure 13. Obviously the Milky Way consists of innumerable points of light. This is a photograph of a portion of Pharaoh's River in the southern hemisphere. It illustrates how rapidly the stars increase in number as that band of light is reached. That dark spot near the center is called the "Coal Sack." It indicates that some obscuring cloud lies between us and those millions of stars. (From a photograph taken at the Harvard College Observatory at Arequipa, Peru, by Miss Margaret Harwood, director of the Maria Mitchell Observatory, Nantucket, Massachusetts. The plate was made with the 1-inch Cooke patrol camera on May 12, 13, and 18, 1923, with a total exposure of 11 hours 39 minutes. It is the region of the Southern Cross, Omega Centauri, and Eta Carinae. Courtesy of the Harvard College Observatory.)

THE NORTH STAR, THE GREAT DIPPER, AND URSA MAJOR

Figure 14. Of course the bear's tail ought not to be so long, but this is a celestial, not a terrestrial, bear. The two stars Beta and Alpha are called the "Pointers" because they point to the North Star. (Slightly modified from Heis, *Atlas Coelestis*, 1872.)

mile or more around you. Then you can count perhaps twice as many lights. You keep using larger glasses, and each time you see twice as many lights as before. Finally there comes a time when your new and larger spy-glass will not show you twice as many lights as the previous one. It will show you more lights, but not twice as many. Then you will say: "At last I have reached the limit of the city. Now I am looking into the suburbs, and soon I will be looking out into dark and almost uninhabited country."

In many directions all over the sky astronomers have explored the extent of the stars. Their work is sometimes like that of the officers of the U.S. Coast and Geodetic Survey when they find varying depths of the ocean up and down the coast and far out to sea; they always find the ocean has a bottom, if they only use a long enough line. In the same way the astronomers find there is always a limit to the group of stars which surrounds us. A sufficiently large telescope will always look beyond that limit out into space, where for millions and millions of miles there are no stars.

When you were standing on the tower near the center of the city, you were using some large glasses so that you could examine the surrounding country, which was almost uninhabited. In several places on the distant horizon you saw a faint glow of light. You could see no definite shape to these faint illuminations. You did not know what they were and thought they

15

might be distant forest fires. Then just before dawn you were given the largest telescope of all, and at once you looked at those faint spots of light on the horizon. Then you found that they consisted of thousands of little sparkling points of light. You realized that we were not living in the only city in the world, for you had found dozens of others far off upon the horizon, and their street lights were shining at night just as ours do. It was a blow to your pride, for you had thought you were living in the only city in all the world.

Besides the stars there are some curious blurred objects called nebulae. They look like little wisps of the Milky Way, or like minute incandescent clouds; hence the name "nebula." It was thought at one time that they were great masses of incandescent gas. Sir William Herschel, about a hundred and fifty years ago, looked at them through a large telescope and found that some of them at least were very distant star-clusters. Now we know that some consist of thousands of millions of stars, and we sometimes call them "island universes."

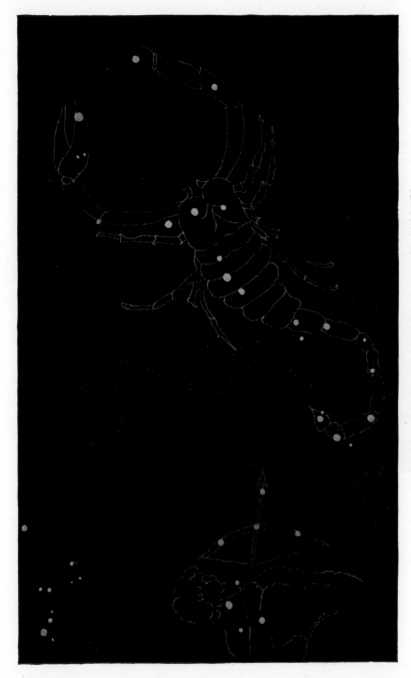

CONSTELLATIONS OF SAGITTARIUS AND SCORPIO

Figure 15. Slightly modified from Heis, *Atlas Coelestis*, Coloniae ad Rhenum, 1872.

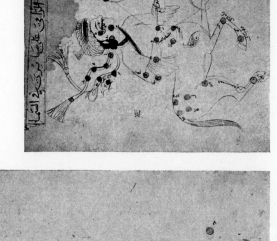

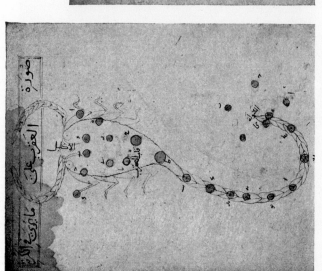

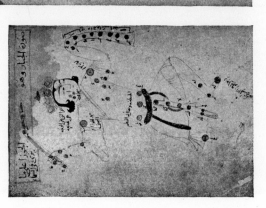

PERSIAN CONSTELLATIONS

Figure 16. About the time when Copernicus was born some one in Persia wrote a book on astronomy and drew these constellations. (Persian, fifteenth century, school of Samarkand, manuscript volume of a treatise on astronomy. Acc. No. 13. 160. 10, neg. No. 21317 LSB, Metropolitan Museum of Art. Courtesy of the Metropolitan Museum of Art.)

III: NAMING
THE CONSTELLATIONS

 IT MUST have been far back in prehistoric times that men and women first noticed that there was a difference in the brightness of the stars. Probably tens of thousands of years passed before they gave names to the different degrees of brightness. The first list of stars which has been preserved and in which each star was given its name and brightness was made by Ptolemy about the beginning of the present era; that is, about 2,000 years ago. Ptolemy was a Greek who lived in Alexandria in Egypt. He belonged to a group of famous scientists and scholars. This early list consisted of approximately 1,000 stars.

The few brightest stars are classed as of first magnitude. The North Star is a typical second magnitude star. The faintest star which you can conveniently see is about the sixth magnitude.

The heavens are divided into constellations, much as the United States is divided into states and Canada into provinces. The first constellations to be named are in the northern hemisphere, because they were named by the Babylonians, Egyptians, and Greeks. Like the eastern states and provinces, the first to be settled, these old constellations have very irregular boundaries. In the southern hemisphere the boundaries of the constellations have only recently been determined. Like the western states and provinces, these newer constellations are bounded by straight lines and right angles.

Primitive men and women thought these groups of stars looked like animals or people. They must have had wonderful imaginations, for it is difficult for us to see much resemblance. In those days people had a number of favorite animals, and these animals were supposed to be governed by spirits. The bears were supposed to be controlled by a great bear spirit, the lions by a lion spirit, and the scorpions by a powerful scorpion spirit, etc. Each tribe, or sometimes each nation, had its favorite animal spirit. The spirits weren't always animals either; sometimes they were mythological men and women. It was natural that primitive man should want to stake out a claim among the stars for the headquarters of his favorite spirit. Some were more fortunate than others in their allotted territory. The scorpion (Figure 15) got a group of stars which looks very much like him. Leo, the lion, got a fair location which resembles a great African lion, at least to a slight extent. Taurus, the bull, found himself in a group of stars which gave him a very good head and horns, but left the rest of the bull's body to your imagination. Gemini, meaning "twins," in the acreage assigned to them

18

THE GREAT STAR CLUSTER OF HERCULES

Figure 17. There may be 100,000 stars in this cluster. It is just barely visible to the naked eye as a very faint blurred star. So distant is this compact city of stars that the light by which you see these stars today left the cluster when the Cro-Magnon race entered Europe and began to draw those wonderful pictures of bison and horses in the caves of France. The light which is leaving this cluster now and starting on its long journey at the rate of 186,000 miles per second will meet our remote descendants in the year A.D. 37931. What kind of country will these light-beams from Hercules find? My guess is that it will be much warmer and people will spend week-ends flying to the Arctic Ocean. (From a photograph of N.G.C. 6205 taken at Mt. Wilson Observatory June 6, 7, and 8, 1910, with the telescope 5 feet in diameter, exposure 11 hours. Courtesy of the Mt. Wilson Observatory.)

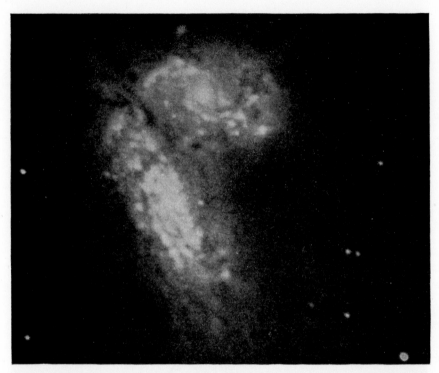

DID THE SUN AND THE WANDERING STAR LOOK LIKE THIS JUST
AFTER THE ENCOUNTER?

Figure 18. Perhaps this photograph represents our sun and that wandering star
after the collision or very near approach. You can faintly trace two spiral arms
on both the sun and the star. It certainly is a time of great confusion with much
luminous matter floating around. Some aggregations already have been formed
and others are undoubtedly being formed. It looks like the origin of two solar
systems as described by Chamberlin and Moulton of the University of Chicago.

There is one serious trouble—this is a real photograph and 10,000 million
years ago photographs weren't invented. These objects are two spiral nebulae
and each contains probably more than a thousand million suns. They have accidentally come together and distorted each other much as the sun and the wandering star did thousands of millions of years ago. The sun and the wandering star
would make two such minute specks of light when they came together and then
separated that they would be entirely invisible on this photograph. Yet on a much
smaller scale it is probable that the sun and star may have closely resembled this
photograph as they started, each to go its own way and develop its own solar
system. (A photograph of the twin spiral nebulae, N.G.C. 4567-8, constellation
of Virgo, taken at the Mt. Wilson Observatory with the telescope 5 feet in diameter, March 22 and May 19, 1914, exposure 6 hours. Courtesy of Mt. Wilson
Observatory.)

by the Babylonians, were two bright stars side by side. The constellations Hercules, Virgo, and Orion bear such slight resemblance to the human form that sometimes I wonder if their associates know where they live.

Of course you know that these constellations are purely imaginary as seen from the earth. You remember that when you see three stars in a row and close together, it doesn't mean that they are close together or really in a row. Two of them may be fairly close together and the third may be very far away. Sometimes on the side of a mountain you see a curious group of rocks which from a certain place looks like a human face. If you move up closer to this group you will find that it is often merely a number of individual bowlders and crags which are scattered over a considerable surface.

There are some interesting stars in the constellations which have no mythical association. Occasionally you will find a star which looks hazy or blurred. Through a telescope these blurred objects become marvelous clusters containing thousands upon thousands of sparkling stars. In the center of such a cluster the stars appear to be so close together that you cannot count them as individuals. One cluster, which is visible to the naked eye in the northern hemisphere, is called the Great Star Cluster of Hercules, for it is in the constellation of Hercules (Figure 17). In the southern hemisphere there is a still more brilliant cluster, also visible as a blurred star to the naked eye. It is called Omega

Centauri, from the Greek letter ω and the constellation of the Centaur (Figure 99). There are scores of these clusters, called "globular clusters," and they are symmetrically located with respect to the Milky Way.

IV: ORIGIN OF THE EARTH

ACCIDENTS will happen even among the stars. Apparently their block signal system occasionally fails to operate, for once in a while two stars will collide or come extremely close together. When you recall that there are over 100,000 million stars in the cluster which we call our Galaxy, it is not surprising that there should be an occasional casualty (Figure 18). Also, those millions and thousands of millions of stars which make our Milky Way are not by any means stationary. They are moving with a speed of many miles per second. We should expect that two stars might occasionally bump each other or at least come so close as to cause great tidal waves on each other's surface.

And indeed the sun and another star either grazed each other's surface or just missed each other as they passed at the rate of many miles per second. It was perhaps 10,000 million years ago that this happened. However, there is some recent evidence to indicate that it was only 3,000 million years ago. This mishap can't be attributed to darkness, for they must have

21

passed in a blaze of light. This seems especially evident when we realize that the commotion set up in each star produced probably several thousand times more light and heat than the sun is giving us at present. If the sun had been accompanied by a previous set of planets, they would have been scorched beyond recognition. Any ancient civilizations would have perished utterly.

We do not know what companions, if any, the sun had before this primeval and, for us, historic encounter; but from the welter of this catastrophe Venus, the earth, Mars, and the other planets emerged. Life ultimately arose on at least one of these planets and perhaps on three of them.

As the sun and the wandering star dashed past each other gigantic waves were raised on each. The waves were so great that they splashed right out into space. A vast amount of the stuff of which the sun is made was thrown away from the surface with such force that it could not return. When the sun met with this terrible accident, it may for a while have looked something like Figure 19.

Probably before many millions of years a great deal of this evicted matter found its way back to the sun, but a considerable amount must have been blown away into space, never to return. Countless numbers of individual atoms and molecules were driven away into the depths of space by the repelling power of sunlight, made temporarily thousands of times more intense.

IS THIS THE SUN WITH A GROWING FAMILY OF PLANETS?

Figure 19. When the wandering star had gone its way, the sun was left in space with a growing family of planets. Those spiral arms, hurled into space by the catastrophe, gradually condensed into aggregations and innumerable meteorites. As the sun was convalescing from the blow, it may have looked something like this picture. Of course this is a photograph of an existing spiral nebula. It has been distorted, too, by an encounter with another nebula. Compared with our solar system this nebula is gigantic. It probably contains more than a thousand million suns. To a planet revolving around one of these suns the others in this nebula would look like the Milky Way. (From a photograph of the spiral nebula N.G.C. 7479 taken at the Mt. Wilson Observatory. Courtesy of Mt. Wilson Observatory.)

A CHAOS OF CRATERS

Figure 20. A giant's no-man's-land where huge meteors may have torn up the lunar surface. That large crater in the upper left-hand corner is Tycho. Like many other craters, Tycho has a mound in the center. In the lower right-hand corner there are formations which look like long straight scratches. They are hundreds of miles long. Although we can see the moon so plainly we know very little about it. (From a photograph taken at the Mt. Wilson Observatory on September 15, 1919, by means of the Hooker telescope, 8 feet in diameter. Courtesy of the Mt. Wilson Observatory.)

A portion of the ejected matter began to revolve around the sun in oval orbits. It was spread out like a flat disc, and from a great distance it may have looked something like Saturn's rings. These snow-white modern rings of Saturn are smoother than were the great parent rings from which the planets came. At first they probably looked something like a stream of clouds (Figure 18).

However fiery hot this matter had originally been when it left the sun, most of it became so cold as to freeze in a comparatively short time. Innumerable small masses consisted of molten rock which promptly froze into small solid rocks; other masses were made of nearly pure liquid iron, and these froze into solid pieces of iron.

Quantities of gases of various kinds were held prisoner inside these liquid and solid pieces of the badly damaged sun, but, of course, a great deal of free gas was blown away by the temporarily intense brilliance of the sunlight. We say "temporarily," because the sun was made unusually bright by the disturbing effect of that passing star. Before long, however, the sun cooled a bit and recovered from the embarrassment of its encounter. Thus its unusual brilliance was but a temporary glow.

For millions and thousands of millions of years this curious procession of large and small bodies of rock and metal continued their endless journey around the sun. Gradually the sun lost its unnatural and perhaps pulsating brilliancy and became the

23

source of almost steady and moderate light we know so well.

Do not think that these millions of annual trips around the sun were monotonous for the pieces of rock and metal. Collisions were the order of the day. Sometimes they came together to form swarms of individual rocks. Then on other occasions they would hit each other with such force as to become welded together. In this way some of the big aggregations grew bigger, for they attracted the little fellows to them. At the same time, perhaps, many of the little fellows were growing bigger also; but they couldn't catch up with the few big ones which had a good and early start.

Maybe the big masses of metal and rock were liquid at first and in a few million years cooled enough to form a hard crust. No matter how hard that crust was, it would not have been a good place to live. First, there would have been no atmosphere of any kind and certainly no free oxygen. There would have been cracks on the surface of such a mass, and some of the hot interior would have flowed through these cracks and over the surface. Many of these eruptions we would have called volcanoes, and as with volcanoes today, many gases escaped from the boiling lava. Today these gases give us nitrogen, water vapor, and carbonic acid gas; but years ago the masses of rock and metal were probably too small to hold the gases. These little molecules of gas, as they became heated by sunlight, developed a speed so great that they could not stay on the primeval ball.

They bounced away almost as fast as they came from the boiling lava. Once clear of the growing ball's immediate attraction, the intense sunlight probably drove them off to the endless stretches of interstellar space.

The second reason why life on such an early mass of meteoric stuff would not have been happy was the danger of being struck by other masses of rock and metal. For millions of years the surfaces of these barren globes of rock and iron must have resembled a no-man's-land. The bigger the ball grew, the more it gathered to itself all the neighboring rocks, now called meteors or meteorites. Some were large, and millions were small; but the impacts dented the surface into craters and splashed molten rock in all directions (Figure 20).

Gradually, by means of these impacts, the large masses grew even larger and ultimately became the planets, from Mercury to Pluto. When they became large, their attractive power increased. Then the heated and vibrating atoms of gas from the boiling lava could no longer bounce away. They remained on the planet's surface and formed an atmosphere. Thus for most of the planets a new epoch in their history commenced, for with the exception of Mercury they continued ever after to go through the universe surrounded by a halo of gas, an atmosphere.

Perhaps some of the globes in the very beginning were so large that they had an atmosphere. Such may have been the history of Jupiter, Saturn, Uranus, and Neptune. It is even possible that the earth had a small atmosphere from the very first.

It may be that our moon, due to its original speed and location, did not fall upon the earth but revolved around it instead. Thus it became the earth's partner and grew as the earth grew (Figure 21). However, it never became large enough to hold an atmosphere, and so, like Mercury, the moon to this day is a barren waste of rock exposed directly to the almost perfect vacuum of space.

Some think that the moon was once a part of the earth. They assume that the earth emerged from the great collision as a ball of liquid rock, iron, and the other substances it now contains. It was not so large as it is now; yet it was large enough to be unwieldy, and when it came near the sun in its annual journey, it was warped into a pear-shaped body by the tremendous attraction of the sun and by the vibrations set up by the rapid spinning on its axis. In time it became something like a dumb-bell with one lobe smaller than the other. Finally it broke, and now we call the smaller lobe the moon and the larger lobe the earth.

When you swing, you can make yourself rise higher and higher by making your body move up and down in the same number of seconds that it takes the swing to go either back or forth. This means that your body is vibrating in sympathy with the swing. Your vibrations combine with those of the

THE EARTH, THE MOON, AND THE SHADOW

Figure 21. Far from the sun and still farther from the stars, the earth and moon revolve in silence around each other. Sometimes they get tangled up in each other's shadow. In this picture the moon is just passing through the earth's shadow. When that happens, people on the earth say the moon is eclipsed. If there were people on the moon they would say the sun was eclipsed. When the moon is eclipsed it seldom entirely disappears. There are enough stray sunbeams in the earth's shadow to give the moon a copper color. (*The Outline of Science*, edited by J. Arthur Thomson, published by G. P. Putnam's Sons, New York, 1922. Courtesy G. P. Putnam's Sons.)

LUNAR APENNINES

Figure 22. That slightly curved line of cliffs which runs almost diagonally across the picture is a chain of mountains, the Lunar Apennines. They rise abruptly from the plain to a height of over 3 miles. When this photograph was taken the sun was shining full upon the cliffs. Below, on the plain, there is a group of three craters. The right-hand one, which is the largest, is called Archimedes; it is 60 miles in diameter. (From a photograph taken at the Mt. Wilson Observatory on September 15, 1919, with the telescope a little more than 8 feet in diameter. Courtesy of Mt. Wilson Observatory.)

swing so perfectly that you swing through greater and greater distances. The strain on the rope also becomes greater, and it is conceivable that the rope might break.

A thin glass bowl will vibrate when it is gently struck. It will then create waves of a certain frequency per second in the air and these waves enter your ear and give a sensation which you call a note of a certain pitch. If at the same time you sound a note of that same pitch on some instrument or even with your voice, it is possible to break the thin glass bowl; for the sound waves from your voice are of exactly the same frequency as the vibrations of the bowl. Your voice waves helped the bowl to vibrate more and more, until finally the bowl could stand the strain no longer and broke.

Swings and bowls are not unique, for almost everything can vibrate. The time required for one vibration varies with the object. In the case of the bowl, each vibration was only a small fraction of a second. The swing, however, took many seconds for one vibration or one swing back and forth. You know from experience that the longer the swing, the longer it takes to make one round trip. Even bridges have a certain period of vibration to which they like to respond. Some time ago, when there were many wooden bridges, it was customary for a procession to break step when it crossed a bridge; for they were afraid that if they kept step to a band of music, they might be all stepping in exactly the "natural" time of vibration of the bridge. In that case the bridge would vibrate more and more as a long procession passed over it, until finally it could stand the strain no longer.

Sir George Darwin and others have computed that when the earth was young and plastic, its favorite time of vibration was very nearly the time between successive tidal waves caused by the attraction of the sun. At that remote epoch the day was much shorter than it is now. Perhaps it was not more than four of our hours. So the solar tidal wave pounded around the earth in nearly the earth's "natural" vibration period. As a result, the earth could not stand the strain of increased vibration and broke. Thus the moon was formed, because the earth could stand the increasing vibrations no longer.

When the earth and moon first separated, they were probably pear-shaped. It may be that they behaved like two gobs of plastic candy which have been pulled apart.

Harold Jeffreys of Cambridge University, England, thinks that the sun and the passing star actually collided and that the moon never was a part of the earth but was merely one of the many primeval balls and ultimately became the earth's partner. He also thinks that the catastrophe to which we owe our existence happened less than 10,000 million years ago.

Here we have two explanations for the origin of the moon. Each is very reasonable. Some day you may decide for yourself which story is the more probable.

If an atmosphere went to school, it would be very poor in ancient history; for it destroys all old records and apparently likes only new and living things. Today on the earth the atmosphere protects life by burning with its friction the millions of small meteors which strike the earth. On the other hand, by causing rain and snow, the atmosphere wears away the mountains until only grassy plains and forests are left. In this way those giant craters, if they ever existed, made by falling meteors millions of years ago, have all been worn away and covered with soil and forests. Not a single ancient crater remains as a museum specimen of the first epoch of the earth's history.

Fortunately, the moon, the earth's junior partner, has kept the record of the archaic epoch of the planet's history. When the surface of the moon is dented, it stays dented for millions of years. There is no atmosphere to carry globules of water into the sky. Therefore, no rain ever falls upon the crags and rocky deserts (Figures 22 and 23). The surface of the rocks on the moon may crumble, due to the intense heat of sunshine during the long lunar day of two weeks and the equally intense cold of space during the long night. This variation in heat may cause expansion and contraction that in time might loosen large slabs from the surface of the cliff and send them crashing to the base of the mountain.

Meteors, large and small, must be pelting the moon incessantly. No kindly blanket of air rubs these shooting stars until they burn up. No stream of sparks announces the approach of a meteor. Almost invisible and in perfect silence, they crash upon the lunar mountains. They must cause havoc, and after millions of years they probably destroy many a cliff. "It is rather strange that with the moon under observation, visual and photographic, for such a long period, no flash of a large meteorite as it struck has been noted," says C. E. St. John.

Yet after all, this damage is slight when compared with the leveling action of rain and snow, rivers and glaciers. So the moon, which has none of these, has stayed like a museum specimen, little altered by the lapse of several thousand million years. If we examine this antique piece of solar system furniture, we find it dented by thousands of craters. Some are very small, and others are a few hundred miles in diameter. Some look like volcanoes, and perhaps they are volcanoes which once upon a time were active (Figure 24). Then others are so large and the rims so low that they give the appearance of great circular plains several hundred miles in diameter.

Yet we do not know that all the moon's craters were formed in this way. At present, serious objections can be made to any suggestion in regard to their origin. Some day the true cause of the craters on the moon may be known, and that day may come soon, when very large telescopes are made and turned upon the earth's partner (Figure 25).

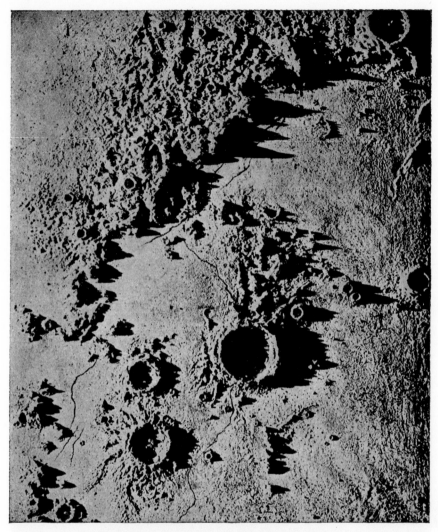

LUNAR APENNINES AND ARCHIMEDES

Figure 23. In this picture the sunlight is coming from the left, so that the cliffs of the Apennines cast their shadows far out over the great plain. Those dark lines in the plain which look like cracks probably are cracks. Their cause, however, is unknown. In the photograph, Figure 71, the cracks also can be identified; but in that photograph they look like snail tracks. However, some of these cracks are half a mile wide. (From a picture in *The New Astronomy* by S. P. Langley, published by Ticknor & Co., Boston, 1888.)

"VESUVIUS AND THE NEIGHBORHOOD OF NAPLES"

Figure 24. This picture is from a photograph of a model of Vesuvius and the many extinct volcanic craters in the neighborhood of Naples. There is a striking resemblance between this model and some of the lunar photographs. Yet it is unlikely that all lunar craters are of volcanic origin. (From a picture in *The New Astronomy* by S. P. Langley, formerly secretary of the Smithsonian Institution, published by Ticknor & Co., Boston, 1888.)

If large meteors caused some of the craters, one would expect to find some scars which were caused by glancing blows. Also one would expect to find some oval craters, where the blow was less glancing. There are a few scars on the moon, but we do not know that they have been caused by glancing blows from meteorites. In the upper part of the photograph (Figure 20), long, straight valleys can be seen, which look as if some giant had scratched the moon when it was soft. Some of the valleys pass through large craters, but in other cases a crater rises from a valley. Plainly as we can see these apparent scratches, we do not know what caused them.

After a few thousand million years the planets drew to themselves nearly all the meteors. In other words, the débris from the great encounter, which originally formed those smoky rings around the sun, came together under the action of gravitation and formed the planets. Now the space around the sun is nearly cleared of all the pieces of rock and scrap metal. To be sure, a few million minute meteors enter our atmosphere every day, and other planets probably have the same experience. But what are a few million shooting stars to planets which have been formed by such titanic forces and from such unnumbered tons of rock and metal?

No longer bombarded by meteors which splash molten rock over continents, Venus, the earth, and Mars had an opportunity to cool. On the earth, at last, the water vapor fell upon the land as rain. No red-hot surfaces drove the water back to the sky in clouds of steam. Therefore, great lakes and then oceans were formed. Then primitive and microscopic forms of life appeared in the sand and warm water.

This is probably the history of the earth, and it may also be the history of Venus and Mars. Remember, we are all explorers. We are trying to make as good a map of the present and past as we can. From time to time you may hear of additions to this story and of alterations, but you may be sure that from decade to decade the story is always approaching nearer to the truth.

NO NOISE, NO WIND, NO STREAMS OF WATER DISTURB THIS DEAD
COUNTRY

Figure 25. A lighthouse keeper would feel at home on the moon, for almost
everything is circular. There are thousands of round craters and scores of round,
flat plains. An artist has tried in this picture to show how the moon would look
if you could walk on its surface.

With no atmosphere to cause haze the horizon is clear and distinct. Also the
stars are shining by both day and night, for there is no blinding glare from the
air to blot out the stars in the daytime. Since there is no air of any kind, of
course there are no sound waves and consequently no sound. The earth is seen
shining by reflected sunlight; the western hemisphere is turned toward you.
(From a picture in *The New Astronomy* by S. P. Langley, formerly secretary of
the Smithsonian Institution, published by Ticknor & Co., Boston, 1888.)

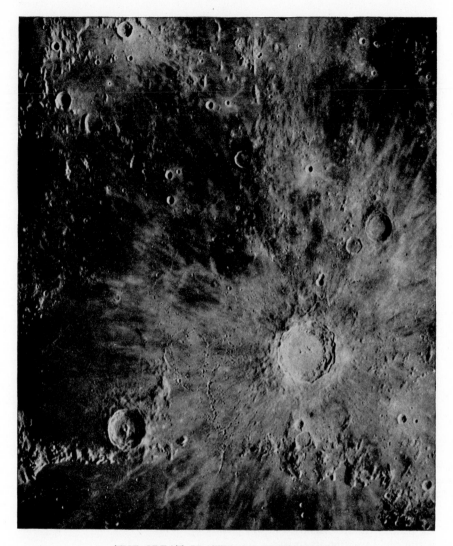

THE GREAT CRATER OF COPERNICUS

Figure 26. If the man in the moon were standing on the floor of this crater at the time when this photograph was taken he would say the sun was nearly over head. It would take him some time to walk to the edge, climb upon the rim, and look over the landscape; for this crater is about 50 miles in diameter.

No satisfactory explanation has ever been made for those white streaks which radiate from Copernicus and many other craters, both large and small. (From a photograph taken at the Mt. Wilson Observatory with the Hooker telescope, 8 feet in diameter, September 15, 1919. Courtesy of Mt. Wilson Observatory.)

V: ELECTRONS AND PROTONS

HAT fiery débris of liquid and gas that came from the sun at the time of the memorable disaster hardened ultimately after millions of years into rock and iron. But what is rock? If you could magnify it ever so much with a magic microscope, what would you see?

Those wonderful Greeks and Romans made a guess. Democritus said you would see a number of minute particles, that all things were made of minute particles—rock, wood, air, and animals. Modern chemists during the last couple of hundred years proved this to be the case. They found there were a little over seven dozen different kinds of minute particles: iron, copper, hydrogen, oxygen, nitrogen, carbon, aluminum, lead, silver, gold, silicon, sodium, and others. Ninety have so far been discovered.

These simple substances are called elements. Sometimes several elements will combine to make a very useful but more complex substance. When two particles of hydrogen combine with one particle of oxygen, a compound substance is made which we call water. Particles, or atoms, as they are called, of

carbon, hydrogen, and oxygen, when combined in certain proportions, make sugar. If the same atoms are combined in
slightly different proportions they make alcohol. Such little
groups of atoms are called molecules. A molecule of water, for
example, consists of two atoms of hydrogen and one atom of
oxygen.

Until recently no one knew what these atoms would look
like if you could examine them through that imaginary and
powerful microscope. It was probably generally assumed that
they were round balls, absolutely indivisible, the very foundation of all real substance.

They were not supposed to be packed solidly together like
a barrel of pebbles. Scientists knew there must be space between them even in the densest of bodies, such as a bar of lead.
They realized that the molecules moved around among themselves. Even in ice there is space between the molecules, and
there is a considerable movement. When ice melts and becomes
water there is a great deal of movement among the molecules.
Finally, when you heat the water so much that it turns into
steam, the molecules at once jump far apart and dart around
at a very high speed. In fact they try so hard to get away from
each other that they sometimes burst the boiler which is holding them.

For a long while, then, we have been realizing that all things
are not so solid as they appear to be. Rocks, wood, and animals

are like that distant smooth band of green which proved to be a forest of trees. To some extent each piece of rock is something like a swarm of bees. At a distance the bees look like a faint cloud and move as a whole very much as a cloud does. Perhaps another swarm of bees of a different kind might shy away from them, much as two balls would bounce away from each other.

When the bees have gathered on a tree and are clustered close together, it is possible to pick up a handful of them and handle them somewhat as you would a snowball.

To an enormous giant who could see immense distances but who was quite blind to minute things near at hand, this handful of bees would look like a solid ball. The swarm of bees would look to him like smoke. If you told him that the "ball" was really a mass of little bodies which were moving among themselves and that there was a good deal of space between them, he would laugh at you and say you had a vivid imagination. Then, if you told him that the smoke was really a swarm of individual bees moving very rapidly and that there was a great deal of space around each bee, he would be more surprised than ever.

It would probably be true that in that ball there was more empty space than there was actual bee-substance; for their wings and legs kept them from packing very closely. In other words, that ball which the giant saw was perhaps four-fifths

35

empty space and only one-fifth real bee-substance. The smoke or swarm may have been ninety-nine hundredths empty space and only one hundredth bee-substance. The giant, of course, was very fortunate in having a little human being with bright eyes to tell him all this. Chemists and physicists have not been so fortunate. It has taken them thousands of years to learn about atoms and the enormous amount of empty space in all things.

In 1911, Sir Ernest Rutherford in England discovered the atom was not so simple after all. He proved it was made of many even more minute particles, called electrons and protons. Later, Niels Bohr of Denmark showed that an atom is very much like a solar system—that is, like the sun and all the attendant planets.

In the center of each atom is a nucleus which consists of protons and usually some electrons. Around this nucleus revolve other electrons just as planets revolve around the sun.

Now we know that all matter—all substance—consists of only electrons and protons. The difference between copper and lead or between one element and another is in the number of electrons and protons, and the combinations of these queer things of which the universe is made.

The simplest of all elements is hydrogen gas, in which one electron revolves around a nucleus. It is as if the solar system consisted of just the sun and Mercury. Next in complexity comes helium—the non-explosive gas used in dirigibles. Two electrons revolve around the nucleus. The sun with just the planets Mercury and Venus represents this miniature solar system. The familiar element carbon, of which coal and diamonds are made, has six electrons which revolve in six little orbits around the nucleus. This can be likened to the sun with the attendant planets Mercury, Venus, the earth, Mars, Jupiter, and Saturn. Nitrogen has seven electrons revolving in seven orbits, oxygen eight, iron twenty-six, silver forty-seven, gold seventy-nine, and finally uranium, the most complicated element of all, has ninety-two electrons revolving in ninety-two orbits around its very heavy nucleus.

Our fathers and our grandfathers realized that no substance could be absolutely solid, that the atoms of which it consisted must have space in which to move. Never for a moment did they suspect the amount of space which really exists. Not only were those atoms farther apart than our ancestors estimated, but each atom, instead of being a small round ball, now is found to be something like a little solar system, or perhaps like a little group of waves revolving around each other in some mysterious fashion. Waves of what? you are asking. We do not know. Perhaps these waves can be imagined as the circular waves in a pond which are caused by a falling stone. This is not strictly true but it may help us to understand these queer things. The centers of these waves, perhaps the cause of

ELECTRONS AND PROTONS

these waves, we call electrons and protons. These electrons and protons are so minute that, compared with their size, they are a long way apart. Yet to us they are all so close together that they cannot be separated with a microscope.

You remember how surprised the giant was when he discovered that what he thought was a cloud of smoke was really a swarm of bees. Now think how much more surprised he would be if he discovered that on account of his poor eyesight he was mistaken—there were no bees. What he took to be a bee really was merely half a dozen specks of dust, and around each speck there were funny waves only half visible. Each speck was no bigger than the point of a pin. These half dozen specks were moving rapidly among themselves, but never getting far from each other. It was because they kept so close together that the giant mistook each group for a bee.

"This is a queer world," the giant said. "I thought that cloud of smoke was very dense, but I found that it was nearly all empty space with here and there a few bees flying very fast. Now with these new glasses I find there weren't any bees there at all. What I took for a bee was merely a few tiny specks of dust, darting around with incredible speed. Yet each little group of specks stays by itself. They don't mix."

Then the giant took a new and better magnifying glass: "Now I can examine each little group of specks," said this quite human giant. "In each group the specks seem to be running around a favorite speck which is in the center. I am going to call those specks in the center protons and those specks which are rushing around, electrons, but I see some electrons are mixed in with the protons."

The distance across the nearly circular path of a typical electron is about 50 thousand times greater than the electron's own diameter. If you wanted to make a large model of an atom, you might choose a golf ball to represent an electron. Then the nucleus or proton must be about half a mile away. It certainly would be true that such an atom would consist almost entirely of empty space. Of course the proportion of space to substance would be the same whether your model were a mile in diameter or microscopically small.

Why don't we sink into the rock upon which we are sitting? How can such an overwhelming proportion of empty space be as hard as iron? The answer is we, ourselves, are also merely airy nothingness. We don't sink into the rock any more than those swarms of bees would mix together. The electrons, revolving around the protons with incredible speed, are the centers of powerful and largely unknown forces.

To some extent they can be compared to a camp of soldiers. The commander has stationed a line of sentries far from the camp. Another regiment may be marching through the country, also with an advance skirmish line from its main column. The skirmish line sees the line of sentries from a long distance and immediately notifies the commander of the regiment. The regiment, therefore, moves in another direction. There was no contact, but the regiment changed its course because of the camp. The camp represented a powerful force, the knowledge of which made the regiment move away.

The camp and the regiment each occupied by means of their sentries and skirmish lines many square miles, while each soldier as he was standing or marching occupied less than a square foot. When you consider the far-flung skirmish lines, the regiment might easily occupy four square miles or 100 million square feet. Hence the space actually occupied by the men was only a minute fraction—perhaps less than one-hundred-thousandth of the space occupied by the regiment.

If you had looked down upon this country from a lofty airplane you would have seen two nuclei of dark bodies. Surrounding each nucleus at long distances you would have seen rapidly moving small bodies. Shall we call them soldier electrons? You watch them approach and you think they are going to come together in a confused mob, for you know that they are merely military formations spread over hundreds of acres of nearly empty land. Instead, you find these two bodies of almost airy nothingness do not even touch each other. Apparently the regiment bounced away from the camp much like a billiard ball. Being in the sky you might not know the reason for these movements. The commander of the regiment, however, knew very well why he changed his course—he felt the danger of that powerful camp.

E. S. Eddington, director of the astronomical observatory of Cambridge University, has described this vast amount of empty space in his book *The Nature of the Physical World* (Macmillan Co.). The old idea of a table, according to Mr. Eddington, was a solid substance. Common sense told our ancestors that it was wood, which could not be easily dented because it was what they called "solid." Therefore, Mr. Eddington's elbow did not dent his table when he leaned upon it. Also his elbow was solid and made of real flesh and bone. This very useful elbow rested comfortably upon the table and didn't collapse.

Yet we know that the table is almost nothing but empty space. Here and there minute specks are dashing about and preventing Mr. Eddington's elbow from denting the surface. It is much like a well-trained football team. The members run around the half back, who has the ball, so fast and so vigorously that the opposing team cannot break through the "interference." Mr. Eddington speaks of this table of dashing electrons and empty space as his "scientific table," and his empty elbow, which will neither collapse nor dent his scientific table, as his "scientific elbow."

But neither Mr. Eddington's furniture nor his elbows are queer, for all our furniture and all our elbows are like his.

ELECTRONS AND PROTONS

Here we must pause a moment and realize that we are understanding this mysterious thing too well. When we think we know something about interstellar space, or the inside of a knife blade, so well that we can whistle it backward, we may feel sure we are quite wrong. Nothing in the real world is ever so simple. In the world of books, life and the universe are often quite simple; but books are merely diaries of our explorers, and the latest chapters in these diaries indicate that electrons, instead of being little hard round balls of electricity, are more like little clouds of particles which behave like waves and are influenced by waves.

They have been compared by George P. Thomson of Aberdeen University to a gossamer spider:

"When this little animal is clinging to the stalk of a plant, it is a small solid object. When it wants to move it shoots out long filaments many times its own length. The wind catches these and wafts it away. I regard the filaments as analogous to the waves which surround the electron, while the body of the spider is analogous to the central point. One can press the analogy further. If the wind carries the spider so that one of its filaments is caught in an obstacle, the spider will be swung around and its path deflected although its body has not hit anything solid.

"In just the same way with the electron, if its waves pass over an obstacle, this modification is transmitted back through the wave system to the electron itself. If we suppose that the elec-

42

tron is constrained always to move in a way determined by the waves in its immediate neighborhood, the motion of the electron itself will thus be modified. The waves act as a kind of intermediary between the disturbing objects and the electron itself. The electron goes where the waves in its immediate neighborhood carry it, just as the spider is pulled by the parts of the filaments which are actually attached to it. But the form of the waves, near the electron, is determined by events at a distance, whose effects are propagated through space in the form of waves.

"A question that inevitably arises is—what is the medium which transmits electron waves? I am sorry that I can give no entirely satisfactory answer. . . ." [1]

This description by Mr. Thomson is one of the best which has been written on this subject, yet it by no means paints a picture which can be thoroughly comprehended. The trouble is, we are dealing with a subject that cannot be visualized. That is, we cannot make a model out of clay or wood or metal, and when you cannot make a model of something or draw a picture of it, then, of course, you cannot visualize it. To a certain extent mathematicians can understand these things without being able to visualize them. You know you would have difficulty in visualizing a simple equation in algebra, yet you under-

---

[1] "Waves and Particles," by George P. Thomson, *Scientific American*, July, 1930; from the George Fisher Baker Lecture delivered at Cornell University and reprinted by the *Scientific American* through the courtesy of *Science*.

stand it perfectly. For example, $3 \times 4 = 6 \times 2$ cannot be represented as a model, for you have not stated what 3, 4, 6, and 2 represent; yet, so far as your experience goes in this three dimensional world, this equation is correct and also is thoroughly understood by you. When we talk about the stars or the inside of a knife blade, we must get accustomed to talking about things we don't understand; because our explorers bring back such imperfect maps, and also because we all have minds too feeble for the real wonders of the world. However, let us continue during this journey down Pharaoh's River, and far off into space, to talk of electrons and protons as if they were little hard microscopic spiders surrounded and influenced by curious waves which no one can really understand. It makes a good beginning in trying to understand the mysteries of this universe. From time to time, as you read about new explorations, you can change your description of the atom; for probably each decade will bring your opinion nearer and nearer to the truth.

MOON 4 DAYS OLD

Figure 27. (From a photograph taken at the Lick Observatory of the University
of California. Courtesy of the Lick Observatory.)

MOON 7 DAYS OLD

Figure 28. First quarter. (From a photograph taken at the Lick Observatory of
the University of California. Courtesy of the Lick Observatory.)

MOON 10 DAYS OLD

Figure 29. (From a photograph taken at the Lick Observatory of the University of California. Courtesy of the Lick Observatory.)

MOON 14 DAYS OLD

Figure 30. Full moon. (From a photograph taken at the Lick Observatory of the University of California. Courtesy of the Lick Observatory.)

VI: THE PHASES OF THE MOON

THAT the moon is round is quite obvious. That it shines by reflected light is perhaps not so self-evident. Yet if you look carefully at the moon you will strongly suspect that it shines only by reflected sunlight; for you will notice that the bright side always is nearest to the sun.

Since the moon travels around the earth we sometimes see the entire sunny side. That is so when we are between the sun and the moon. Then we say the moon is full. About one week earlier than full moon we can see only one-half the sunny side. We call this appearance the "first quarter."

When the sun is shining almost straight down into a moon crater, there are no shadows, or at least very short ones. Down in the tropics here on our earth the shadows at noon are very short, because the sun is shining straight down from almost right overhead. If you look at that big crater called Copernicus in Figure 26 you will see that the shadows are short. This is because to a man in the moon standing in that crater the sun would be almost overhead. On the other hand, in Figures 27

45

and 28, where the daylight and darkness meet on the left-hand edge of the crescent, the shadows are so long that they extend entirely across a crater. They are like the long shadows on the earth at sunset or sunrise.

From one full moon to the next is about 29½ days. The moon is so far from the earth—nearly a quarter of a million miles—that the journey from one full moon to the next is long, and nowadays very uneventful. To meet her new moon, quarter moon and full moon appointments, the moon has to travel over its path at the rate of over half a mile a second. (Figure 34).

If you think that the moon has a long journey to make every 29½ days, you must agree that the earth has a still harder time; for keeping always about 90 million miles from the sun, it must make the circuit of its nearly circular path every year. To accomplish this it must move over 18 miles per second. Such a speed is more than thirty times as fast as a rifle bullet or cannon-ball. Yet it was always thought the earth stood still until the clever Greeks discovered that it is moving. But the Greeks did not know how very fast it is moving. So again we find that appearances are very deceptive.

MOON 19 DAYS OLD

Figure 31. (From a photograph taken at the Lick Observatory of the University
of California. Courtesy of the Lick Observatory.)

MOON 2I DAYS OLD

Figure 32. Last quarter. (From a photograph taken at the Lick Observatory of
the University of California. Courtesy of the Lick Observatory.)

MOON 23 DAYS OLD

Figure 33. (From a photograph taken at the Lick Observatory of the University of California. Courtesy of the Lick Observatory.)

THE DARK SHADOWS AND THE BLINDING LIGHT OF THE SUN

Figure 34. It looks as if the earth had four moons, but we already have learned that things are not always as they seem. Our moon from time to time occupies each of these four positions. When the moon is just between us and the sun, the moon's shadow covers a small part of the earth. If there are people living on that part of the earth, they say the sun is eclipsed; for to them the sun is hidden by the black disc of the moon. Two weeks later the moon may enter the earth's shadow and then shine as a faint copper ball. When this happens, we say the moon is eclipsed. Imagine standing on the earth and looking at the moon when it is in that extreme left-hand position. From your point of view the moon would be about half illuminated and half dark. You would say the moon was a crescent and nearly half full. If you crawled over to the other side of the earth and looked at the moon when it was in the position indicated by the extreme right-hand drawing, then you would see the moon more than half illuminated, but not quite a "full moon." Perhaps you would say the moon was about three-quarters full. (*The Heavens,* by Amédée Guillemin, published by Richard Bentley, London, 1867.)

VII: GRAVITY

HE laws of falling bodies are very interesting to every one, especially to one on an icy path. People had only hazy ideas on this subject until Galileo dropped some balls from the Leaning Tower of Pisa (Figure 35). It was about three hundred years ago that the famous Italian scientist found that a piece of wood would fall from the top of the tower to the ground in about as short a time as a piece of iron. A ten-pound piece of lead will fall as fast as a one-pound piece of the same metal, except for a very slight effect due to the resistance of the air. Also you know that the faster you go in an automobile, the greater is the pressure of the wind against the windows. The air has the same effect upon a falling body; it tends very slightly to slow up its motion.

Everything falls toward the center of the earth, if it is given a chance. The speed of the fall has nothing to do with the material of which the thing is made. Old Mother Earth is impartial and treats everything alike.

There is a mysterious force which makes an apple fall from a tree, and which also compels the moon to revolve around the

47

earth. Sir Isaac Newton called this force "gravity" and said that it behaved as if the earth attracted the apple and the moon. We do not know what this thing called gravity is. Newton was the first to tell us how it behaves, and Einstein is the latest to describe it, and in still greater detail. We say that because of gravity the earth attracts a falling apple, or that the sun attracts the earth and thereby compels the earth to revolve around it. We do not mean that the earth and sun act like magnets. We merely mean that there is a mysterious force associated with the earth and sun and all bodies which makes them behave as if they were attracting each other.

The apparent attraction of the earth is very strong, as you well know when you try to jump over a fence. It is fortunate for us that it is, for otherwise we might slip off the earth entirely and find ourselves floating around in space and having great difficulty in breathing.

The longer gravity acts on a ball which is free to fall, the faster the ball will go. When Galileo dropped a rock from the Leaning Tower of Pisa, it fell 16 feet at the end of the first second. It started of course at rest and kept on increasing its speed until at the end of that first second it was going at the rate of 32 feet per second.

The automobile has made us familiar with the word "rate"; for we all know what is meant by "the car went at the rate of 22 miles per hour." This statement of course means that

GALILEO GALILEI (1564-1642)

Figure 35. Italy's most distinguished physicist and astronomer. It was in Pisa, the town in which he was born, that Galileo made his most famous observations. Even if the tower of Pisa had not leaned on account of a defective foundation, it would have been famous; for Galileo from this tower proved that all bodies fall with equal velocity regardless of their weight, if we except the effect of the resistance of the air. It is interesting to find that as late as 1597, over fifty years after the death of Copernicus, Galileo wrote to Kepler and said that while he believed the sun was the center of the solar system he dared not make his belief public more from fear of ridicule than from fear of persecution.

Galileo was the first, so far as we know, to examine the stars with the newly invented telescope. Consequently he discovered that there were mountains on the moon, that four satellites revolve around Jupiter, that Venus presents phases like the moon, that the Milky Way is not a smooth band of light, but consists of innumerable stars, and that there are sometimes spots on the sun. (Reproduced by permission of the University of Chicago Press. Courtesy of the Yerkes Observatory.)

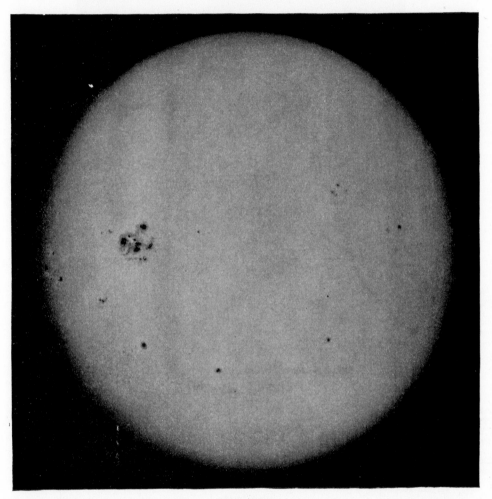

THE SUN

Figure 36. This is the great mass from which the earth came and which effectually controls our planet's movements. It is also a star of which thousands of millions make a spiral nebula. No wonder such great star clusters attract each other when they consist of bodies built on such a colossal scale. (From a photograph taken at the Yerkes Observatory of the University of Chicago; reproduced by permission of the University of Chicago Press. Courtesy of the Yerkes Observatory.)

the car went so fast that if it continued at that rate of speed for a whole hour (3,600 seconds), it would travel a distance of 22 miles (116,160 feet). If a car went 116,160 feet in 3,600 seconds, then it would go a little over 32 feet in one second, or its speed would be at the rate of 32 feet per second.

By an interesting and very simple method the distance a rock will fall at the end of any number of seconds can be determined. Also the velocity the rock will have after any number of seconds can be figured. For a few seconds they are as follows:

Number of Seconds	Total Distance Fallen	Velocity at End of Each Second
1	16 feet	32 feet per second
2	64 "	64 " " "
3	144 "	96 " " "
4	256 "	128 " " "
5	400 "	160 " " "
6	576 "	192 " " "

You can sometimes get an approximate idea of the height of a cliff by dropping a rock and noting the number of seconds it takes to fall. If it takes 3 seconds, the height is evidently about 150 feet. If you fall from a second-story window, it will take you about 1 second to reach the ground, and when you do reach it you will be going at about 22 miles per hour.

We know how gravity behaves, but we do not know what this mysterious thing is. Its effect varies with distance just as light does. If a body is moved twice as far away from you as it was, it will seem to attract you with only one-quarter the force; if three times farther off, one-ninth, etc. The moon is 60 times as far from the center of the earth as we are. It is, therefore, affected by the earth with only $\frac{1}{3600}$ as much force. Instead of falling toward the earth 16 feet at the end of one second, it will fall only one thirty-six-hundredth as much, or five one-hundredths of one inch (0.05 inches). However, the moon is moving through space at a very considerable rate and the combination of falling toward the earth, and also trying to keep on a straight path through space, makes it go around the earth in an oval curve called an ellipse. This path is the moon's orbit.

You probably are wondering why the moon should try to go through space in a straight line. If you do ask this question it will not be an easy one to answer. We will try, however, to make some kind of answer. A long time ago the great Sir Isaac Newton said that if a body is once given a push in space it will go in a straight line forever, unless something comes along to move it to one side. We already have heard of two different theories, either of which would explain what gave the moon a push and started it off through space. Whether or not these theories are correct, most astronomers agree that it was only a few thousand million years ago that the moon began to revolve around the earth in such a way that it never hits the earth and never flies off in a straight line as it would like to do.

In the same way the earth is going around the sun in an ellipse, and takes one year to make the journey.

Primitive man thought that this motion was reversed. To him the earth was standing still and the sun was going around it. Since he also thought the earth was flat, he had considerable difficulty in imagining what happened to the sun when it set in the west. Some thought it was carried in a chariot through passages under the earth so that it again could rise in the east. Some of the Greeks were very wise. Pythagoras claimed the earth was round. Aristarchus, according to Archimedes, announced that the earth revolved around the sun. Erotosthenes measured the earth's diameter. Unfortunately for us, the work of another Greek, Ptolemy, was used by the Europeans during the Dark Ages. Ptolemy thought the earth stood still and was the very center of the universe. For more than a thousand years our European ancestors entertained this foolish notion. It was not until about four hundred years ago that an astronomer in Poland, Copernicus, announced that the earth and all the other planets went around the sun.

Still men were very much puzzled. Why did the earth go around the sun in that peculiar path called an ellipse? They thought that there must be some kind of spirit animal which guided the planets around the sun. They even went so far as to think of these spirit animals as having something of the shape of whales.

GRAVITY

Finally, Sir Isaac Newton of England, about two hundred years ago, proved that gravity applies to all things, not only on the earth but in the heavens. He showed that due to the sun's apparent attractive power the planets must go in paths which are ellipses.

Although Newton destroyed those spirit whales, he created another mystery—what is gravity? The answer to that question still is unknown.

So far as we know, the power of gravity extends to the most remote star in the sky. Of course, at such inconceivable distances, the effect of one star upon another is exceedingly slight. On the other hand, there is an unlimited time during which this effect can be exerted. When you start to pull any heavy load, you know it moves extremely slowly at first, but the longer you pull the faster it goes, until finally it is moving at a reasonable speed. Stars behave in this same way. Those brilliant island universes are apparently moving hundreds of miles per second.

From another point of view it is not so surprising that the island universes are moving in various directions. They apparently are being drawn by mighty forces, even though the cause of these forces may be very distant. For example, all the stars in our group of galaxies, and there are thousands of millions of them, are apparently pulling these island universes.

It is strange that a mere speck of light, invisible to the naked eye and barely visible in the most powerful telescope, can have a very great effect. However, each speck of light is really as large and about as fiery-hot as our sun. Many of them are vastly larger and hotter. Again, compared with the earth, the sun is inconceivably a giant. Our earth seems large to us—eight thousand miles in diameter, if we go straight through to China. Our sun, on the other hand, is more than 800,000 miles in diameter, over one hundred times greater (Figure 36). Its apparent attractive power, its gravity, is so great that a sun-man, who wanted to spend one second in falling, would be obliged to jump out of a window on the thirtieth floor, instead of a second-story window on this earth. When this sun-man landed on the surface of the sun after his one second's fall, he would be going over six hundred miles per hour—five times as fast as an ordinary airplane. Such is the size and apparent attractive force of the sun where a body falls, not sixteen feet, but four hundred and forty-four feet during the first second.

There are millions of island universes, each with thousands of millions of stars like our sun. No wonder the island universes move about among themselves and gather here and there in groups.

VIII: MERCURY

AR back in the remote past it was discovered that there were two kinds of stars; "fixed stars" and those which move and apparently wander among the "fixed stars." The wanderers were thought to be gods. We still call many of them by names of the Greek and Roman gods, such as Mercury, Venus, Mars, Jupiter, and Saturn (Figure 39). What these wandering stars could be, if they were not gods and goddesses, was a mystery for thousands of years. It wasn't until the invention of the telescope, about 300 years ago (about A.D. 1608), that we knew they must be huge, round bodies very similar to the earth and moon. Then it was clear that two of them at least, Mercury and Venus, were cold, and shining like the earth and moon by reflected sunlight. Soon it was proved that the same thing was true of all the planets.

Naturally, the side of the planet which is away from the sun is in darkness, just as the side of the tree which is away from a campfire is in darkness. When that salamander was leaving the sun, all the planets must have appeared as bright round discs,

54

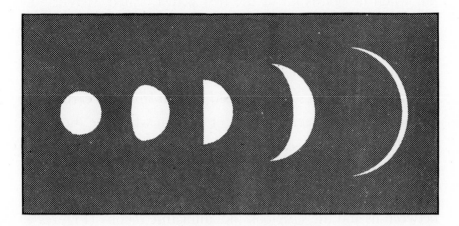

THE PHASES OF MERCURY

Figure 37. When Mercury is on the other side of the sun from us, we see the whole or nearly the whole illuminated side. Then the planet looks round like the full moon, but since it is far off it looks small. It is like looking at some one facing you but on the opposite side of a camp fire. You can see the whole face of your friend illuminated by the flames. Such a view of Mercury is the very left-hand picture.

At some other time Mercury may be to the left of the sun as seen from the earth. Only one-half the illuminated disc would then be visible, and Mercury would look as it does in the middle picture. If your friend moved a quarter way around the camp fire and kept facing the flames, you would see only his profile. His head would be only half illuminated. His face only would be bright, for the back of his head would be in darkness. He would represent the "half phase" of Mercury in the middle picture.

As Mercury moves around the sun and gets almost directly between us and the source of our light, he presents more and more of his dark side toward us. Therefore we see less and less of the bright side which must always face the sun. Thus Mercury becomes an ever thinner crescent until finally, when it is directly between us and the sun, it disappears entirely. When Mercury is between us and the sun it is much nearer and therefore the thin crescent appears larger. (From a picture in *The Heavens*, by Amédée Guillemin; publisher, Richard Bentley, London, 1867.)

but when he got as far as the first planet, called Mercury, he probably noticed that the sun's rays lighted only one side and that the other half was in darkness. This didn't surprise the salamander, for he often had noticed that only that part of the moon which was in sunlight could be seen from the earth. Also he remembered a recent eclipse of the sun when the moon got directly between the earth and the sun. He well remembered that the side of the moon which was toward us was black.

In a telescope, the planets Mercury and Venus, which are between us and the sun, look like miniature moons (Figures 37 and 40). Sometimes we see them as thin crescents, at others as half moons, and then again as nearly full moons.

Mercury is so small and so near the sun that it is seldom seen. Since Mercury's orbit is the smallest of all the planets, it is clear that we never can see Mercury very far from the sun. Obviously, we cannot see Mercury in the daytime, so we must look for it just after sunset or just before sunrise, though, even then, twilight and clouds near the horizon make it very difficult to see.

The Greeks thought that there were two stars: one, which they called Apollo, appeared in the east just before sunrise, and the other, which they called Mercury, was seen only in the west just after sunset. When we found that these two stars were really the same planet, we gave it the name of Mercury. The Egyptians were as badly mistaken as the Greeks and gave separate names to the two appearances: Set and Horus.

Mercury is much smaller than the earth and would be an unpleasant place in which to live. It is so near the sun that the heat must be terrific, but from our point of view it has a still more serious defect; it has either no air at all or extremely little. Also, so far as we know, it always presents the same side toward the sun. It accomplishes this by slowly turning as it travels around the sun. If a certain unknown mountain on Mercury enjoys the blinding light of the sun, it will continue to have that pleasure through all the ages. It is much as if one side-stepped around a camp fire, so that he always faced the fire.

The planet Mercury keeps the same side always toward the sun, because the sun has made it revolve in that way. Several thousand millions of years ago when Mercury was young and plastic, the sun pulled it so hard by means of gravity that it became a little warped and bulged a bit in the direction of the sun. It became just a trifle egg-shaped. Then the gravity of the sun tended to keep one of the bulging sides always facing it. The sun couldn't accomplish this at once. However, through millions of years the sun, by continuously acting on these bulging sides, made Mercury spin more slowly on its axis. As the spinning on its axis grew slower, the day on Mercury grew longer and longer, until finally one side was left always in darkness and the other side always in light.

Mercury is not the only body to behave in this way. If you look at the moon through a field glass, opera glass, or spyglass of any kind, you always will see the same bright mountains and the same dark plains, month after month. In this case, it was the powerful attraction of the earth that warped our satellite and made it very slightly egg-shaped.

In order to understand why Mercury has no air, we must refer again to Mr. Eddington's scientific table. It would be very convenient if every one had a duplicate of that table in his study, for we must remember that iron, wood, and even human beings are mostly empty space. As you might guess, the air is much more empty than that scientific table or than we are. The atoms of oxygen and nitrogen have plenty of elbow room in which to dart about. Although they frequently bump into each other, they manage to develop a very considerable speed.

We already have discovered that what we call heat is largely the degree of nervousness of these atoms or groups of atoms. We are prepared then to believe that the air we breathe is full of very rapidly moving atoms. We can imagine air 100° below zero (Fahrenheit). Then the ultimate particles would be very much more sluggish than they are in the ordinary air which we breathe. So long as we are imagining, let us imagine the air so cold that the atoms do not move at all. That would certainly be the very coldest temperature that it would be possible to have. It is possible to compute this temperature on the ordinary thermometer scale. It is 469° below zero (Fahrenheit). In the laboratory some things have been made so cold that they were only about 3° (Fahrenheit) above this absolute zero, as this complete lack of heat is called. Even when the temperature of a body is at absolute zero, and the atoms themselves are still, inside of them the little electrons continue running around their protons at their usual tremendous speed.

If a body at absolute zero were left in your study and you made no effort to keep it cold, its atoms would soon acquire increasing motion from contact with the surrounding air, and in a comparatively short time they would be rushing past each other and bumping into each other with the same speed as the particles which make this paper or your hand.

If your study were rather chilly, if its temperature were 32° (Fahrenheit), the small particles of oxygen which you are constantly breathing would bounce from one another with an average speed of almost 2 miles per second. This is only the average speed. Many atoms of oxygen would strike, bounce and strike again with a speed several times greater. As you heated up your room to make yourself more comfortable, the speed would increase.

It is a curious fact that all atoms do not have the same speed when they are subjected to the same degree of heat. Oxygen, nitrogen, and water vapor, the three chief gases of our air, all behave about alike. On the other hand, helium gas, which we use in dirigibles, will bounce from one collision to another with about twice their velocity. Some helium atoms may have a speed of 25 miles per second.

Gravity seems very powerful when we are climbing a steep

hill. A cannon-ball goes up into the air with tremendous force. It leaves the ground at the rate of less than a mile per second and then always falls back to the earth, because gravity is so powerful. Do you think this would always be true? Would a cannon-ball always return to the earth no matter at what terrific speed it started? It certainly would not; there would come a time when it would leave the surface of the earth and never return. It can be proved that if a cannon-ball were shot up into the air with a velocity of about 7 miles a second, it would never return. For millions of years it might wander through space like a meteor. Since war is getting out of fashion, it is not likely that we shall ever make so powerful a cannon.

It is true, then, that if a cannon-ball could be shot up into the air with a velocity of more than 7 miles a second, it never would return to the earth, and what is true of a cannon-ball also is true of an atom. If, after thousands of millions of collisions, an atom finds itself in the upper air, perhaps 150 miles from the earth's surface, it may be going at so great a speed that the gravity of the earth cannot pull it back. Through interminable time it may wander through space, perhaps around the sun, perhaps out in the great dark spaces between the stars. On the other hand, its independent career may be cut short by Old Mother Earth. A year later the earth may overtake it, and attract it so strongly that it will once more become a part of our air.

We must be thankful for two things: that our earth is so large that no atom can bounce away unless it has a speed of more than 7 miles a second, and that our most valuable gases, oxygen, nitrogen, and water vapor, are slow and seldom exceed that critical speed when they are high up in the sky. But we have probably lost, in this way, a great deal of helium and hydrogen. Even at the temperature at which water freezes, a hydrogen atom has an average speed of more than 7 miles per second, which means, of course, that many hydrogen atoms must have a speed several times larger. If we were living on Mercury we could not be so thankful. A cannon-ball with a velocity of only 2 miles per second would leave that planet forever. This unfortunate state of things is due to the smallness of Mercury. Its attractive power is so slight that a body falls only about 4 feet during the first second. The blinding sunlight on Mercury would make an oxygen atom nervous. His excitable nature would cause many of his comrades to run about, collide and bounce at a speed much in excess of 2 miles per second. It was in this way that Mercury lost its air—lost all the gases which from time to time were emitted by its volcanoes. Of course there may be some gases left, but we can find no trace of them.

IX: VENUS

HE earth has a twin sister called Venus. The trouble is that they don't know each other very well. At least, the earth knows very little about Venus, who travels a lonely path around the sun between the earth and Mercury. Venus is lonely from our point of view because she has no moon.

These two neighboring planets are almost exactly the same size. Venus has the inside path in going around the sun, and therefore receives more heat.

As we watch Venus from night to night we find she never gets very far from the sun. We must see her in the western sky, just after sunset, or in the eastern sky before sunrise. On those occasions Venus is exceedingly brilliant and can frequently be seen to cast a shadow. The Greeks were as mistaken about Venus as they were about Mercury. Thinking there were two stars, they called the morning star Phosphorus, and the evening star Hesperus. It is a year and seven months between successive appearances of Venus as evening star, and the same interval between successive appearances of Venus posing as Phosphorus.

62

Like Mercury, Venus presents all the phases of the moon and for the same reason (Figure 38). She shines by means of reflected sunlight so that we sometimes see her in the telescope as a thin crescent, sometimes as a half Venus, and sometimes as a nearly round bright disc like a full moon. Once in a while

VENUS IN CRESCENT PHASE

Figure 38. This photograph shows how Venus appears when seen through a telescope 40 inches in diameter. Apparently we are looking down upon fleecy clouds, for it is very seldom that even faint marks are visible. (From a photograph by E. E. Barnard at the Yerkes Observatory of the University of Chicago; reproduced by the courtesy of the University of Chicago Press. Courtesy of the Yerkes Observatory.)

Venus comes directly between us and the sun. Then we see her projected against the sun as a black disc, for naturally the side toward us at that moment is perfectly dark.

Venus is so well clothed in fleecy clouds that as she moves over her orbit we cannot tell how often she turns around. Some astronomers have thought that she turns around about as often as the earth does. Others have believed that Venus always presents the same side to the sun. At the Mt. Wilson

Observatory, St. John and Nicholson have made a very careful investigation of this subject and find that Venus certainly takes longer than 10 or 15 of our days to turn once on her axis, and she may take much longer (*Astrophysical Journal,* Vol. LVI). In all her ways Venus is as difficult to understand as was her namesake among the Greek goddesses.

The principal reason for this investigation on Mt. Wilson was to find out more about the atmosphere on Venus. If you wish to think of Venus as inhabited by thinking animals, the result of this very careful piece of research is discouraging; for St. John and Nicholson found no evidence of either oxygen or water vapor. Apparently, in its early youth, no planet ever had much free oxygen. The oxygen always was combined with carbon and made carbonic acid gas, which came mostly from volcanoes and meteors. When life first appeared in the form of primitive germs on the earth, it had to get along as best it could without much oxygen. After a while certain kinds of plants absorbed the carbonic acid gas. They retained the carbon and let the oxygen go free. Then other forms of life, such as fishes and animals, were developed, which depended upon free oxygen just as we do. Therefore, when we find evidence of free oxygen in the atmosphere of a planet, we suspect that it may have been caused by the green cells in plants and seaweed. Conversely, when we don't find any evidence of free oxygen, we are inclined to think that life, if any, must be extremely primitive.

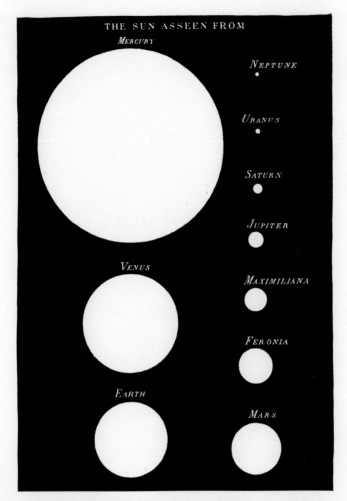

IT ALL DEPENDS UPON YOUR POINT OF VIEW

Figure 39. We like to think the size of the sun as seen from the earth is standard. It looks like as if life would be intolerably hot on Mercury and equally unbearably cold on Neptune. It wouldn't be so bad on either Venus or Mars. Between Mars and Jupiter there are many, perhaps thousands, of very small planets called "Asteroids." Some are no bigger than a city and there are probably thousands so small they never have been seen. Feronia and Maximiliana are names of two asteroids. Judging by the small size of the sun as seen from one of these asteroids, a boy on such a distant rock would have to exercise to keep warm. (*The Heavens,* by Amédée Guillemin; published by Richard Bentley, London, 1867.)

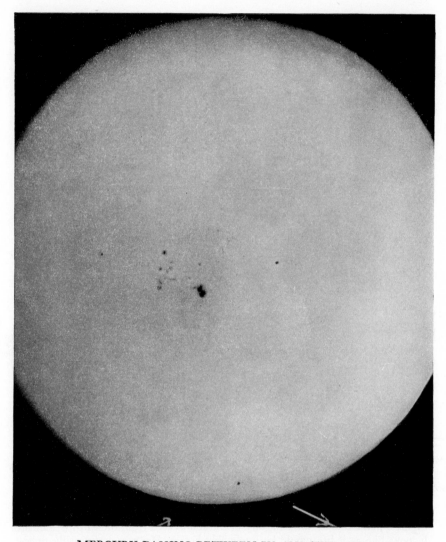

MERCURY PASSING BETWEEN US AND THE SUN

Figure 40. We see only the dark side of Mercury when it is directly between us
and the sun. In the photograph the left-hand arrow points to a tiny speck which
is our innermost planet. However, this minute speck is 3,000 miles in diameter.
Mercury's apparent motion was toward the lower right-hand corner, as shown
by the right-hand arrow. Several of the sun-spots are obviously much larger than
Mercury. (From a photograph taken at the Yerkes Observatory during the tran-
sit of Mercury, November 14, 1907; reproduced by the courtesy of the University
of Chicago Press. Courtesy of the Yerkes Observatory.)

Henry Norris Russell, Chairman of the Astronomical Department of Princeton University, found, some years ago, that there was good reason to believe that the atmosphere of Venus was rare, perhaps only one-tenth the density of our air. We would consider such a lack of air so absolutely intolerable that we would be obliged to lie down and die. Yet, in 1,000 million years, little germs might develop into animals or plants, or both, which would enjoy such a rare atmosphere. However, the lack of oxygen and water is a very grave objection to the probability of life on Venus.

It may be that when we look upon the plain white crescent of Venus we are seeing upper layers of clouds of dust driven hither and thither by winds which blow over a barren and desert country. The atmosphere may be mostly nitrogen (N) and carbonic acid gas (CO_2).

A desert country, burned by intense heat, and filled with stifling gases, which are raising perpetual clouds of dust, is perhaps a description of our nearest neighbor.

X: MARS

 HE best-advertised star in the world is Mars. It must have been one of the first planets discovered by prehistoric man, for its decidedly red color, and at times its great brilliancy, make it one of the most conspicuous objects in the sky.

During modern times speculation concerning the inhabitants of Mars has been incessant (Figure 41). We have seen them pictured in the "movies" and described in novels. H. G. Wells, in a fascinating and imaginative story, assumed that they came to the earth. Therefore it is with unusual interest that we examine Mars, in order to find out whether conditions are at all favorable for life in any form with which we are familiar.

Mars is farther from the sun than is the earth, and receives less light and heat. It doesn't necessarily follow that Mars is colder, for you know that here on the earth we have great changes in temperature, although all places are approximately the same distance from the sun. For example, it is exceedingly hot in Death Valley in Southern California, and at the same

66

time the neighboring mountains may be covered with ice.

The amount of air a planet has seriously affects the temperature of the surface. If there is little air, the planet is cold for the same reason that the top of a mountain on the earth is cold. On the other hand, if there is plenty of air and if the planet is reasonably near the sun, the surface will be warm, at least when it is exposed to sunlight. Air behaves much like the panes of glass in a greenhouse. It lets in the light but prevents the heat from escaping. At least the air lets most of the sunlight come down to the earth and it holds the resulting heat long enough to make us reasonably warm.

Perhaps it is unfortunate for the Martians that they are both farther from the sun and have a less dense atmosphere than the earth. Still, it may be that they are looking at us and pitying us for living at the bottom of such a dense sea of air. If there are Martians, they probably say: "If the intense heat and sultry days on Venus and the earth haven't killed all the animals, these conditions at least must have made them very stupid. The animals on such planets probably have brains only a little better than fishes."

If an atom of air in the upper parts of the Martian atmosphere has a velocity of more than three miles a second, it will probably bounce away and perhaps never return. On Mercury this so-called "velocity of escape" is only about two miles, while on the earth and Venus it is in the neighborhood of seven miles.

MARS

Since Mars is larger than Mercury, it can hold its atmosphere; also, since it is smaller than the earth, its atmosphere is less dense at the surface.

Mars probably has less than half as much air as we have. To us such an amount of air would be unbearably rare; we would have as much difficulty in breathing there as we do on the tops of our highest mountains. But perhaps our fishes wonder how we can live in such a rare substance as the air, where they would die in a very short time. It all depends upon custom and the point of view.

The most prominent feature of Mars is the appearance of the brilliantly bright polar caps. They look and behave much like the snowfields on the earth. During the Martian winter they grow large, and then during the summer they either disappear or become exceedingly small.

On the earth, in the northern hemisphere, the shortest day is about December 21st, but our coldest weather comes a month later. In the same way, June 21st usually is our longest day in the northern hemisphere. However, we all know that we get our greatest heat in July. This same effect is noticed on Mars. The polar cap will have its greatest extent some time after the shortest day for that hemisphere.

Since we can measure the temperature of a furnace by analyzing its light, and since we have found the temperature of the sun, it will not seem surprising that we know the temperature of Mars. At noon on Mars during the Martian summer, the temperature is about 50° Fahrenheit. At night, however, Mars must have a degree of coldness which we can measure only in our laboratories. The white polar caps are probably 90° Fahrenheit below zero.

In the telescope, Mars is of a red or orange color with a number of dark greenish spots of irregular shape (Figure 42). Also there are a vast number of minute spots, some of which are so arranged that in small telescopes they give the appearance of straight lines. These imaginary lines, often called canals, are really optical illusions. Of course, we do not know what the rows of exceedingly faint spots are.

When the Martian spring approaches and one polar cap begins to grow smaller, a band of dark green appears on the edge of the white polar cap. Then those rows of exceedingly faint spots appear near the pole, according to Percival Lowell of the Flagstaff Observatory. As the season progresses these apparent lines can be seen extending farther down from the pole, until finally, in summer, they reach the equator. They are very, very difficult to see, and consequently there has been a considerable discussion in regard to how many there are and just where they are. Observers differ to such an extent that some claim to have seen a great many fine lines, while others claim that they have never seen any.

A microbe on Mars must not only be able to endure intense

cold, but he must live on a desert and breathe very, very little oxygen. There is only about one-thirtieth as much moisture in the air of Mars as there is in the air above Pasadena, California. If luxurious vegetation depends upon moisture it is difficult to see how Martians can boast of a flower garden. However, we generally think that vegetation gives free oxygen to an atmosphere by breaking up the carbonic acid gas (CO_2). So we have come to believe that where we find evidence of oxygen in a planet's atmosphere, we are justified in assuming that there may be vegetation. Such seems to be the situation on Mars. There is oxygen in the air, but not very much. When mountain climbers attempt to reach the top of Mt. Everest, they find it necessary to carry cans of condensed oxygen, for there is so little in the air at that enormous elevation. On Mars the situation is even worse, for it has been found that the Martian air contains only about two-thirds as much oxygen as we find above Mt. Everest.[1]

[1] Contributions from the Mt. Wilson Observatory, No. 307, by Walter S. Adams and Charles E. St. John.

IMAGINARY SCENES ON MARS

Figure 41. H. G. Wells imagined Mars was ruled by very intelligent animals who walked on their hind legs as we do. Since the air is very light, the winds are perhaps not as strong as they are here, so the trees grow tall with very slender trunks. The pull of gravity is so slight that the buildings can be tall with graceful balconies, according to the artist. Of course these pictures are pure imagination. (Pictures from "The Things That Live on Mars" by H. G. Wells, *Cosmopolitan Magazine,* 1908. Courtesy of the *Cosmopolitan Magazine.*)

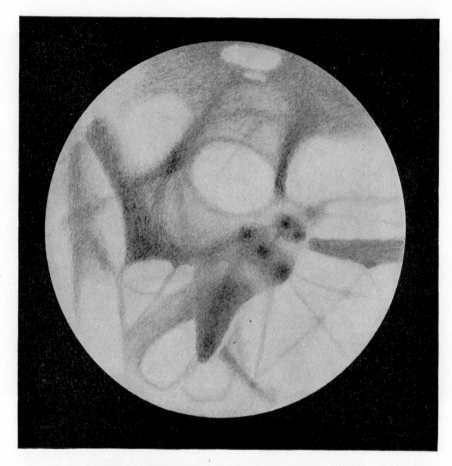

MARS AS SEEN FROM THE LICK OBSERVATORY

Figure 42. That oval white spot on the top of the drawing is the polar cap. The faint straight lines and the round dark patches where the lines intersect are plainly visible. (From a drawing by R. J. Trumpler at the Lick Observatory of the University of California, September 11, 1924. Courtesy of the Lick Observatory.)

XI: JUPITER

HE king of the gods on Mt. Olympus took for himself the largest planet. Jupiter was his name, according to the Romans, and Jupiter still is the name of this wandering star.

The almost circular path of this planet is next beyond the orbit of Mars. When you reach Jupiter you are getting far away from the sun—almost 500 million miles away—so that the path is very large. It takes Jupiter a long time to make the circuit, nearly 12 years.

If that salamander, who visited the sun, should ever visit Jupiter, he would marvel at the size and beauty of this king of the planets (Figure 43). Next to the sun it is the largest body in the solar system, for Jupiter is almost 90,000 miles in diameter, eleven times greater than the earth's diameter. It has, therefore, about 150 times more square miles of surface than the earth. What a planet it would be to explore and map! We have only seven continents, yet there are vast stretches of land in nearly all of them into which no white man has ever penetrated. That is particularly true of North and South America, and even parts

71

of the United States. If the earth were as large as Jupiter, there might be 1,050 continents to explore, for there are seven continents here on the earth, and there might conceivably be 150 times as many on such an imaginary planet. It would take thousands of years to map such a maze of continents. We would probably find strange animals and many interesting fossils.

If any one lives on Jupiter, he must be as queer as any prehistoric fossil that has ever been discovered, for there is a dense atmosphere which always is full of yellow and red clouds. One great spot appeared during the last century and lasted many decades. It moved over the surface as if floating in a fluid medium. It was a huge affair, much larger than all the seven continents of the earth. It now has disappeared. We do not know what has become of it.

Astronomers used to think that all this turmoil was due to heat. They thought Jupiter was still hot and had not had time to cool off. We now know that it is cold, but we do not know why it should be so different from the earth and Mars. Perhaps when Jupiter was formed, it received a combination of material which is different from that which we have in the earth. Later we will find that his great distance from the sun may have helped to give Jupiter a different assortment of rocks and liquid from that with which we are familiar.

As soon as Galileo looked at Jupiter with a telescope he found that it had four moons. Now we know there are nine moons, and perhaps some day we will discover more by means of very large telescopes. A very curious thing was noticed about these moons as early as 1675. A Danish astronomer, Roemer (Figure 44), found that the eclipses of the moons as they occasionally entered the shadow of Jupiter were too early, according to the predicted time, when the earth was between the sun and Jupiter. Then, when the earth was on the other side of its orbit so that the sun was between it and Jupiter, the eclipses of the moons always came later than he expected. In other words, when the earth is nearest to Jupiter the eclipses take place about eight minutes earlier than the average time of occurrence. On the other hand, when the earth is farthest from Jupiter—180 million miles farther—the eclipses occur about eight minutes later.

This was a very puzzling situation. Why should the distance of the earth from Jupiter make the eclipses of Jupiter's moons come sometimes earlier and at other times later? Could it be possible that light takes time to travel? If so, it must take 16 minutes to cross the earth's orbit. At that time, in 1675, nearly every one thought light was instantaneous and paid little attention to this amazing discovery by the Danish astronomer.

The velocity of light, 186,000 miles per second, now is determined more accurately here on this earth; but eclipses of Jupiter's satellites still are observed, and much valuable information is derived from them.

XII: SATURN

EXT beyond Jupiter, as we travel from the sun, is the bright planet Saturn (Figure 45). To the Babylonians and Greeks, Saturn represented the outer limit of the solar system; for the planets which are still farther from the sun are too faint to be seen with the naked eye. These very distant planets were not discovered until after the telescope was invented, which was in comparatively recent times—about the time of the founding of Jamestown in Virginia. Saturn is a very white star as he wanders among the constellations. Even if he has lost the prestige of the Greek god Saturn, he has retained the name. He is distinguished among his associated planets, for he carries through space some wonderful rings. Of course the ancients knew nothing of this unique feature, for the rings were not discovered until a fairly good telescope was made in 1655. Galileo saw two spots of light on each side of Saturn with his little telescope in 1610. Some years later, Saturn was in such a position that the rings were edgewise as seen from the earth. Then they became invisible on account

GANYMEDE AND ITS SHADOW

Figure 43. One of Jupiter's moons, called Ganymede, is close to Jupiter toward the lower left-hand corner of the photograph. Ganymede's shadow is the round black circle on the face of Jupiter. (From a photograph taken at the Mt. Wilson Observatory, March 15, 1921, with the Hooker telescope 8 feet in diameter. Courtesy of the Mt. Wilson Observatory.)

ALAUS ROEMER (1644-1710)

Figure 44. A Danish astronomer who was so far ahead of his time that he was not so much appreciated by his contemporaries as he was by those of following generations. There had been idle discussion as to whether light was instantaneous, as gravity is supposed to be, or whether it took time to travel. By observing the eclipses of Jupiter's satellites, Roemer proved that light required a number of minutes to cross the earth's orbit. We now know that it takes light about 8 minutes to come to us from the sun. However, it was some time before Roemer's demonstration was accepted. (Courtesy of the Yerkes Observatory.)

of their thinness. This disappearance puzzled the Italian astronomer, who suggested that perhaps the planet was following the example of his namesake and eating his own children (Figure 46).

Some people think that Saturn is the most beautiful object in the heavens. A snow-white globe surrounded by equally white rings makes it a mysterious as well as fascinating planet. At first the rings were thought to be a thin sheet of solid rock. However, it soon was realized that such a ring would break into many pieces just as a flywheel of an engine will break if it is allowed to revolve too fast.

The tendency of a revolving body to fly away from the center is called centrifugal force. When a wheel revolves too fast, the spokes are not strong enough to hold the rim, which breaks and flies away, sometimes with great force. The same principle is illustrated by the sling-shot. The faster you swing the string around, the harder the stone tries to break away, so that when you let go, or if the string breaks, the stone will fly off to a considerable distance.

The rings of Saturn we now know really consist of innumerable small bodies. There are so many of these particles, and they are so close together, that they seem to us to be a smooth white ring. You remember that the Milky Way looks like a smooth white band, yet in the telescope we see only a countless number of stars. Unfortunately, our telescopes are not large enough to see the separate bodies that make up the rings of Saturn. Yet we know that they are there.

J. E. Keeler of the Lick Observatory of the University of California made an examination of the light from the inner edge of the ring by means of prisms or their equivalent. Then he determined how fast the inner edge of the ring was moving. Then he did the same thing to the light from the outer edge of the ring, and found that it was moving much more slowly. This is as it should be, if the ring consists of individual bodies which are moving around Saturn in orbits. Furthermore, the speeds found by Keeler are exactly those that the attraction of Saturn would require in accordance with the laws of gravity.

Of Saturn itself little is known. It is obvious that we are looking down upon a very extensive atmosphere. Apparently we see only the faint outlines of clouds or streams of clouds. Those prevailing winds called trade winds, which we find here on this earth near the equator, might present a similar appearance if they could be seen from a great distance. The belts on both Jupiter and Saturn look much like prevailing winds in their dense atmospheres.

Saturn is a large planet. It is about 70,000 miles in diameter, which is 9 times greater than the earth's diameter. This dimension makes Saturn over 700 times greater in volume. You would, therefore, expect that the planet would be approximately 700 times greater in weight. That, however, is not so; for

Saturn has only about 100 times more real substance which, if it could be placed on the earth, would be said to have weight. This means that Saturn is made of very light material; so light as to be less than three-quarters as dense as water. In the center it is undoubtedly more dense, and on the surface less dense than water. It might be difficult, if we were there, to tell where the atmosphere ends and the body of Saturn commences. To swim on Saturn might be like trying to keep afloat in a huge glass of chocolate soda.

No little molecules or atoms of Saturn's atmosphere ever wander off to visit either Uranus or Jupiter. Even if it is light, and perhaps half gas and half liquid, its great size gives Saturn tremendous attractive power. The velocity of escape is about 20 miles per second. In the intense cold of the outer layers of its atmosphere, it is very improbable that many little molecules or atoms can develop such a speed.

Saturn takes nearly 30 earth years to travel once around the sun; like Jupiter it has 9 moons.

XIII: URANUS, NEPTUNE, AND PLUTO

HE planets Uranus and Neptune were unknown to the Babylonians and Greeks. Since they can be seen only by the aid of a telescope they were not discovered until recently. They both carry out the tradition of Jupiter and Saturn in being large. These outer planets are all much bigger than the planets near the sun, such as Mars, the earth, and Venus. Also, like Jupiter and Saturn, these two outermost planets lack that density which we find so convenient when we walk on the surface of the earth. Their average density is only a little more than that of water. This means probably that they must be considerably more dense than water at the center, and very much less dense than that liquid at the surface.

In the turmoil during which the planets were formed, Uranus and Neptune, like Jupiter and Saturn, probably got more than their share of some very light-weight material.

Apparently we see only layers of clouds floating in dense atmospheres which rest on curious and perhaps liquid surfaces. No very brilliant sunlight tries to get through these clouds, for

78

these two outermost planets are a long distance from the center of the solar system. Uranus (Figure 47) is nearly 20 times farther from the sun than the earth is, and Neptune is 30 times farther. Consequently, their paths around the sun are enormously long. It takes Uranus over 80 years to make the circuit, and Neptune over 160 years. At such great distances the sun would appear to be much smaller than it does to us, but its intense brilliance still gives a fair amount of light. Daylight on Uranus is equal to about 1,500 full moons here on the earth. Sunlight on Pluto has the intensity of about 400 times that of our moon as seen from this earth.

Uranus was discovered in 1781 by Sir William Herschel with one of his powerful telescopes, and occasionally is seen by the naked eye. Neptune, however, made our acquaintance, as a known astronomical body, in a much more romantic manner.

For some time it had been known that no one could predict just where Uranus was going to be among the stars. It didn't behave as it would behave if influenced only by the sun, Jupiter, and Saturn. It was, therefore, suspected that there might be another planet beyond Uranus. Perhaps the attraction of this unknown planet was causing Uranus to diverge a little from its predicted path.

Leverrier, a French astronomer, undertook to locate this unknown planet (Figure 48). His problem was to determine at what place in the solar system such a planet would have this disturbing effect upon Uranus. Having no observatory at his disposal, in 1846 he sent the following message to the German astronomer, Galle, at the observatory at Berlin: "Direct your telescope to a point on the ecliptic in the constellation of Aquarius, in longitude 326° and you will find within a degree of that place a new planet, looking like a star of about the ninth magnitude, and having a perceptible disk." [1] The planet was promptly found by Galle within nine-tenths of a degree of the predicted place.

In the meanwhile, another astronomer, J. C. Adams of England, also had solved the problem and located the unknown planet. Like Leverrier, Adams had no telescope with which to verify his figures. He, therefore, notified Challis, at the astronomical observatory of Cambridge University. After some delay Challis began to observe the stars in the neighborhood of the predicted place in order to find if any star was changing its position. Before the Cambridge astronomer had completed this survey, the news arrived of the discovery by Galle at Berlin.

It was later discovered that Challis at Cambridge had actually observed Neptune twice in his survey, but did not recognize it as a planet. The German astronomer, Galle, had a great advantage; for he had a new chart of the faint stars in that neighborhood. When he compared the chart with the sky, he very soon found a star which was not recorded. A few hours' obser-

[1] From *Astronomy,* by Russell, Dugan, Stuart; Ginn and Company, publishers.

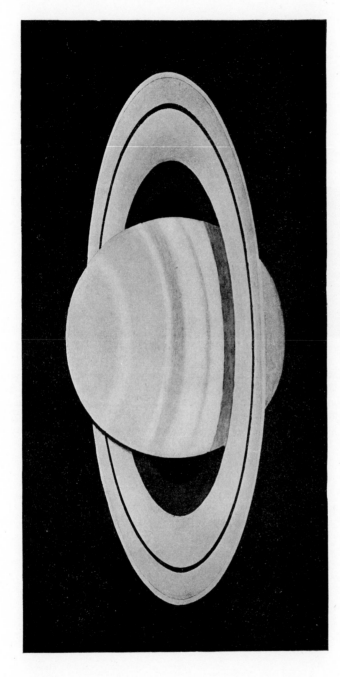

SATURN

Figure 45. Many people think Saturn is the most beautiful object in the sky. (From an excellent drawing made by J. E. Keeler, January 7, 1888, at the Lick Observatory of the University of California. Courtesy of the Lick Observatory.)

AN UNUSUAL VIEW OF SATURN'S RINGS

Figure 46. Now we can see how thin Saturn's rings really are. This drawing represents the appearance of Saturn once in about fifteen years, when we pass through the plane of his rings. (From a drawing by E. E. Barnard made at the Yerkes Observatory of the University of Chicago. Drawn December 12, 1907, by means of the 40-inch telescope; reproduced by permission of the University of Chicago Press. Courtesy of the Yerkes Observatory.)

URANUS AND TWO OF HIS MOONS

Figure 47. Uranus has four moons, but only two of them are visible on this photograph. Although Neptune and Uranus are of about the same size, four times the diameter of the earth, the satellites of Uranus are small, being only a fraction of the size of our moon or that of Neptune. (From a photograph taken at the Yerkes Observatory; reproduced through the courtesy of the University of Chicago Press. Courtesy of the Yerkes Observatory.)

URBAIN JEAN JOSEPH LEVERRIER (1811-1877)

Figure 48. One of France's most illustrious astronomers. He was born at St. Lo in Normandy and educated in the Ecole Polytechnique. At the suggestion of Argo, the director of the Paris Observatory, Leverrier studied the irregular motions of Uranus. He concluded, there was an unknown planet causing the trouble. Galle, of Berlin Observatory, in 1846 discovered this planet, afterward called Neptune, in almost the exact place predicted by Leverrier. In 1854, Leverrier was made director of the Paris Observatory and was twice given a gold medal by the Royal Astronomical Society of Great Britain. (Reproduced by permission of the University of Chicago Press. Courtesy of the Yerkes Observatory.)

vation showed that this unmapped star was moving and was, indeed, the predicted planet, later called Neptune (Figure 50).

Neither Leverrier nor Adams knew that the other was trying to solve this problem. It was a situation that was similar to the definite formulation of some of the laws of evolution, independently, by both Darwin and Wallace.

Even after the discovery of Neptune, Uranus failed to occupy its predicted position with all the accuracy that was expected of it. Again astronomers suspected that another planet beyond Neptune was causing these apparent irregularities. About 25 years ago Percival Lowell began a long series of computations to find the probable position of a distant planet which might be causing Uranus to deviate slightly from its predicted path. In 1929, the Lawrence Lowell telescope was installed at the Lowell Observatory at Flagstaff, Arizona, and a set of photographs was made of the stars in the region where this unknown planet was supposed to be.

The method used was to compare two photographs taken at different dates and search for some star which had changed its place by even a very small amount. This work was done by means of a microscope. Early in 1930, a faint star was found on the photographic plates which moved among the stars at about the speed which a planet beyond Neptune would be expected to have, and not far from the place predicted by Percival Lowell. It proved to be a ninth planet, about 40 times as far from the sun as the earth is and traveling in an oval orbit around the sun in about 250 years (Figure 49). At this rate it takes about four months to travel through the sky a distance corresponding to the apparent diameter of the moon. The director of the Lowell Observatory has given the name Pluto to this new and outermost of the major planets.

Pluto is so far away that no telescope has as yet seen it as a round disc. Even through the 8-foot telescope at the Mt. Wilson Observatory it is a mere point of light like a star. It is possible that this is only one of a number of planets which may be in the remote and semi-dark borders of the solar system.

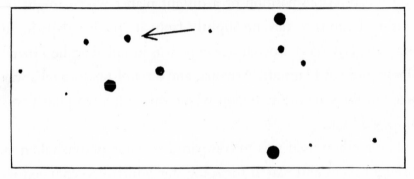

PLUTO

Figure 49. The black dot, to which the arrow points, is the latest addition to the solar family. This is that outermost of all the planets, Pluto. It was discovered at the Lowell Observatory at Flagstaff, Arizona. Percival Lowell had computed the place in the sky that a planet beyond Neptune should occupy. It was while systematically searching for this outer planet, that Pluto was discovered. (From a photograph taken at the Mt. Wilson Observatory, Pasadena, California. Courtesy of the Mt. Wilson Observatory.)

NEPTUNE AND HIS MOON

Figure 50. Discovered by Lassell in 1846 this is Neptune's only moon; for Neptune is like the earth in having but one satellite. This little point of light on the photograph is really about two thousand miles in diameter, which is almost exactly the size of our moon. Neptune, however, is more than four times the diameter of the earth. (From a photograph taken at the Yerkes Observatory, October 10, 1900; reproduced by permission of the University of Chicago Press. Courtesy of the Yerkes Observatory.)

WHERE THE GIANT METEOR STRUCK ARIZONA

Figure 51. "From rim to rim, Meteor Crater measures four-fifths of a mile. It is 570 feet deep. Millions of tons of stone were pulverized and splashed out, creating the numerous mounds encircling the crater. The specks on the (right) edge are stone blocks weighing thousands of tons. Some think there is a mass of meteoric iron weighing about ten million tons buried 1300 feet below the far edge of the crater. According to F. R. Moulton, the great bulk of the meteoric iron has turned into gas by the tremendous heat caused by the blow when this meteor fell and dug up the earth. It behaved like a high explosive shell and made a crater not unlike those made by shells from giant cannon. This visitor came and then became a permanent resident about the time when the Greeks were learning that the earth was round, and were keeping their records in the famous library at Alexandria. ("The Mysterious Tomb of the Giant Meteorite," by W. D. Boutwell, *National Geographic Magazine*, June, 1928. Photograph by James Stokley from a transcontinental airplane. Courtesy of Science Service.)

XIV: METEORS
AND SHOOTING STARS

THE sky was full of shooting stars on the night of November 13, 1833. All the stars seemed to be rushing from one place to another and apparently thousands filled the sky.

Some people claimed the falling stars were as thick as snowflakes. Like sparks from a pinwheel on the Fourth of July they seemed to be shooting away from a point, and that point was in a group of stars called Leo, the Lion.

Many people believed that the world was coming to an end, that the heavens were falling, and that soon the earth would be destroyed by these balls of fire. All during the night this display of fireworks continued. In countless thousands the shooting stars appeared to be bursting through a hole in the sky and in their mad rush seemed to carry all the stars with them even to the very horizon. An eyewitness in South Carolina wrote:

"I was suddenly awakened by the most distressing cries that ever fell on my ears. Shrieks of horror and cries for mercy I could hear from most of the negroes of the three plantations, amounting in all to about six hundred or eight hundred. While earnestly listening for the cause I heard a faint voice near the door, calling my name. I arose, and, taking my sword, stood at the door. At this moment I heard the same voice still beseeching me to rise, and saying, 'O my God, the world is on fire!' I then opened the door, and it is difficult to say which excited me the most—the awfulness of the scene, or the distressed cries of the negroes. Upwards of one hundred lay prostrate on the ground —some speechless and some with the bitterest cries, but with their hands raised, imploring God to save the world and them. The scene was truly awful; for never did rain fall much thicker than the meteors fell toward the earth; east, west, north, and south, it was the same." [1]

There have been other displays of celestial fireworks in which some shooting stars struck the earth. When this happens we call them "meteors," and when we see them in the sky and they do not strike the earth we call them "shooting stars."

At Cone Butte, in Arizona, there is a huge hole in the earth— four-fifths of a mile across and nearly 600 feet deep (Figure 51). The rock on the edge has been jammed up into a lofty ridge 150 feet above the surrounding level. This vast cavity is not the crest of a volcano nor the bed of a sunken lake. It is the hole made by a huge meteor, or a group of meteors, that several thousand years ago struck the country we now call Arizona.

[1] From *The New Astronomy,* by S. P. Langley.

"THE FACE OF THE RIM"

Figure 52. "Dark-red iron stains in the white rock identify meteoric iron within the crater. Digging usually discloses a badly rusted object called a 'shale ball,' the nucleus of which is nickel-iron. Twenty-nine of the ninety known elements, which are nature's building blocks for water, land, and air, have been found in the meteorites. The fragments from the meteor crater region contain 93 per cent. iron, 4 to 8 per cent. nickel, and carbon, phosphorus, cobalt, sulphur, and silicon. There also are small quantities of platinum." (From "The Mysterious Tomb of a Giant Meteorite," by W. D. Boutwell, *National Geographic Magazine*, June, 1928. Courtesy of the U. S. Geological Survey.)

"A PEBBLE FOR CYCLOPS"

Figure 53. "On the eastern extremity of the rim of Meteor Crater stands the largest of the limestone bowlders tossed out. Huge rocks are found half a mile from the crater." (From "The Mysterious Tomb of a Giant Meteorite," by W. D. Boutwell, *National Geographic Magazine*, June, 1928. Courtesy of the U. S. Geological Survey.)

Only tribes of Indians roamed over the plains in those days, so we do not know what happened when this celestial cannon-ball struck.

We can guess, however, that if there were people in that country, all of them within hundreds of miles must have thought there was an earthquake. With the shaking of the ground there must have been a blinding flash of light. The heat was terrific, so that as far as the horizon all life, both plant and animal, must have been destroyed (Figures 52 and 53). Even today the rocks on the side of this hole are burnt and crumbled.

About twenty years ago, Siberia was bombarded by scores of meteoric stars both great and small. Fortunately for human life, this group of meteors struck Siberia in a very remote region. So far as we know only trees and animals were destroyed by the withering blast. A Russian expedition in 1927 described what had happened. They stated that there had been a great forest which extended for 15 miles around the spot where the meteors struck the land.

"The trees are now all bare without bark or limbs and almost all lie on the ground with their tops turned away from the center of the spot, thus giving a sort of fan effect which is plainly visible from the tops of some of the surrounding mountains. Here and there some tree trunks still stand and in a few isolated and very sheltered spots, some are still living. But the region in general is now most desolate.

METEORS AND SHOOTING STARS

"All the vegetation shows the effect of uniform and continuous scorching, which does not in the least resemble the consequences of a forest fire. The scorching is visible on the moss and bushes as well as the trees and some signs of it appear as far as six to ten miles from the center."

The central area is covered with innumerable craters which vary from one yard to fifty yards in diameter. An eyewitness, S. B. Seminov, described the event, although he was 60 miles from the place where the shooting stars struck the earth.

"About 8 o'clock in the morning, I had been sitting on the porch with my face to the north and at this moment in the northwest direction appeared a kind of fire which produced such a heat that I could not stand it. . . . And this over-heated miracle, I guess, had a size of at least a mile. But the fire did not last long. I had only time to lift my eyes and it disappeared. Then it became dark and then followed an explosion which threw me down from the porch about six feet or more . . . but I heard a sound as if all houses would tremble and move away. Many windows were broken, a large strip of ground was torn away and at the warehouse the iron bolt was broken. . . ." [1]

Nearly every museum has some of these meteors—these strange visitors—in captivity. We know that they are made of rock or iron, and that some weigh only a few pounds and others

[1] "The Great Siberian Meteorite," by Charles P. Olivier, University of Virginia, *Scientific American,* July, 1928.

A PIECE OF THE GREAT ARIZONA METEOR

Figure 54. In the neighborhood of the crater made by the Arizona meteor and in the pulverized stone on the rim, hundreds of pieces of meteoric iron have been found. This is a photograph of a piece which is kept at the Yerkes Observatory at the University of Chicago. (Reproduced by permission of the University of Chicago Press. Courtesy of the Yerkes Observatory.)

ANOTHER PIECE OF THE ARIZONA METEORITE

Figure 55. This fragment of the 10-million-ton meteorite weighs 1087 pounds. It is one of a large collection of meteorites which is exhibited at the American Museum of Natural History of New York City. (Photographed by J. Otis Wheelock, Nov. 8, 1906. Courtesy of the Am. Museum of Natural History.)

many tons (Figures 54, 55, and 56). But exactly what are these meteors which have bombarded the earth, and where do they come from?

There are millions of millions of shooting stars in the neighborhood of the sun and earth. They are moving around the sun very much as the earth does. Since they are cold they shine only by the light of the sun. They are so small, however, that that amount of reflected sunlight is insufficient to enable us to see them. We can see the moon because that body is so much larger, although it shines only by reflected light from the sun. Therefore, shooting stars are for the most part invisible until they enter our atmosphere; and millions of them enter every day.

These shooting stars rain down upon our atmosphere in much the way pellets of ice fall upon your car as you drive through a sleet storm. Compared with your car, the earth gets more than its share of meteors. Imagine all the iron of your car to be very much magnetized so that it would attract a nail from a considerable distance. Then let us imagine that instead of little pellets of ice you found little pellets of iron raining down through the air. Under these conditions you would expect your car to be hit many more times per second than it was during the sleet storm.

The earth by means of its gravity gathers millions of these small particles of rock and iron which are moving around the sun in various paths. It draws some to one side and forces them to fall into the earth's atmosphere. They plunge into the air at tremendous speed, sometimes nearly 40 miles per second. The friction with the air is so great that they become not only hot, but white hot. Therefore we can see them, for they are momentarily incandescent; they look like balls of fire.

If they were alive they wouldn't realize how fast they were going. They would merely think that they had been struck by a furious wind which was first heating and then actually blowing off all the rough edges on their surfaces. We don't always know how fast we are going until we hit something. For example, the earth is moving around the sun at the rate of more than 60 thousand miles per hour, and yet in our daily experiences we think of the earth as standing still. As a meteor moves through space he might be as ignorant as we have been in the past. He would see the sun, moon, Venus, Mars and Jupiter, and an occasional comet, moving past him and around him in curious paths. He would probably consider that he was the center of the whole universe, which had been created for his amusement.

Suddenly he has a new sensation. He finds a strange gas called air rushing over his surfaces at the rate of more than 60 thousand miles per hour. Without knowing it he has plunged into the earth's atmosphere. We find it difficult to stand erect against a wind which is blowing only 60 miles an hour. Therefore, it is not hard to imagine that the rough edges of our wan-

88

dering meteor first become hot, then white-hot, and then are torn off entirely.

A meteor spends a fairly active life in the few seconds he exists as an incandescent body in our atmosphere before he strikes the solid earth. Fortunately for us, in most cases the minute particles called shooting stars are all worn completely away before they reach the surface of the earth. Occasionally, some big fellow gets down to the land. Often such a meteor will explode, or apparently do so, making a loud report which sounds like a distant clap of thunder.

XV: COMETS AND METEORS

I
N ALL ages comets have been mysteries to mankind. Like most unexplained things, they usually were associated with evil spirits. People used to think that comets brought pestilence, war, and death. While we have ceased to fear comets, we find many of their queer ways quite difficult to understand (Figure 57). Most comets are faint and seen only by means of a telescope. They usually are little round patches of light, like a bit of luminous cloud. On the other hand, some comets are wonderful objects with a bright head and long graceful tail.

Whether large or small, they all move around the sun. Their paths generally are very elongated ovals, and so long that it sometimes takes a comet hundreds of years to travel once around the sun. One comet, which visited us in 1914, requires 24 million years to make one journey around the sun. This comet was named after its discoverer, and is called Delavan's comet. Its previous visit to the earth was in the Oligocene period when our ancestors looked like gibbons, and horses

LARGEST METEORITE IN CAPTIVITY

Figure 56. This monster weighs 36½ tons. It is kept in the American Museum of Natural History, New York City, and there now is little chance that it can escape. After wandering through space for billions of years it landed in Greenland. The Eskimos called it Ahnighito. (Photographed by K. C. Lenskjold, February 26, 1920. Courtesy of the Am. Museum of Natural History.)

A COMET SEEN THROUGH THE CLOUDS

Figure 57. Daniel's comet of 1907. (From a photograph taken at the Yerkes Observatory of Chicago University on September 8, 1907 with a 6-inch lens; reproduced by permission of the University of Chicago Press. Courtesy of the Yerkes Observatory.)

were small, with three toes in place of a hoof. When this comet is farthest from the sun, it is outside the solar system and about halfway to the nearest fixed star.

There is good reason to believe that the head of a comet consists of a swarm of little pieces of rock or iron, or perhaps of both (Figure 58). Apparently these pieces of rock and metal contain a great deal of gas, which is held prisoner within the solid substance. When this swarm of millions of particles approaches the sun, the gas is in part set free by the action of sunlight. Then it is illuminated by the sunlight, and, in some unknown way, also shines by its own light. It is this atmosphere of luminous gas that makes the comet's head look like a small cloud.

Sunlight has set free many of the imprisoned atoms of gas. As if it were at once dissatisfied with its work, it proceeds to drive these atoms off into the interminable depths of interstellar space. All light has a certain repulsive power and tends to drive minute particles in the direction in which it is traveling. It is a very slight force, so slight that a particle must be so small as to be invisible to the eye to be much affected. However, when the particles are small, and when the light comes from an intensely hot body like the sun, this repulsive force can be very considerable.

The luminous gas, liberated by the sunlight and then driven away like smoke, makes the beautiful comet's tail (Figure 59).

Naturally, as the comet goes around the sun the tail always points away from that central source of intense light (Figure 61).

The solid particles which make the head of the comet probably are very small. Perhaps most of them are smaller than ordinary marbles. They move through space much like a swarm of bees. It is only when they come near the sun that the gas held by these particles is liberated and then driven away by the repelling power of sunlight.

When this swarm of particles comes near the sun it is subjected to great strain by the tremendous gravitational power of that enormous body. This tends to distort the swarm and spread it out in its path. In the course of ages, after many such experiences, most swarms are elongated to such an extent as to become invisible (Figure 60). "The brilliant comet which used to visit us regularly every few years has disappeared," people say. Then as the elongation continues the millions of particles become nearly uniformly distributed throughout their orbit. Unless interfered with by some planet, they will continue to stream around the sun for perhaps millions of years.

Such a stream—a disintegrated comet—is invisible to us unless the earth in its travels happens to plunge into it. When such a collision occurs we have a "shower of meteors."

The most remarkable of these meteor showers occurred on November 13, 1833, which we already have described in Chap-

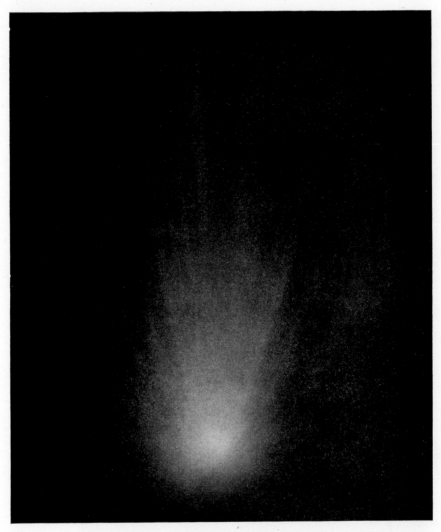

THE "CLOSE-UP" OF A COMET'S HEAD

Figure 58. This is introducing Comet Brooks, so named because W. R. Brooks discovered it in 1911. Evidently there are millions upon millions of atoms and electrons in the comet's head which don't like sunlight, for they are being driven off into space in long straight streams. How you would enjoy a short visit to a comet so that you could see exactly what is happening! (From a photograph of Comet Brooks, 1911, V; taken October 21, 1911, at the Lick Observatory of the University of California. Courtesy of the Lick Observatory.)

A FULL LENGTH PORTRAIT OF COMET BROOKS

Figure 59. The comet was moving through the sky while this picture was being taken. The telescope was made to follow the comet so as to record a clear, well-defined image. Therefore the stars appeared on the plate as little lines or trails. Conversely, if they had been photographing the stars and had ignored the comet, then "Brooks" would have been blurred. (From a photograph of Comet Brooks, 1911 V, taken October 21, 1911, at the Lick Observatory of the University of California. Courtesy of the Lick Observatory.)

ter XIV. Eyewitnesses said there were so many meteors that it seemed as if all the stars were falling. Probably several hundred thousand meteors pelted the earth on that occasion.

Imagine you are walking from one large building to an-

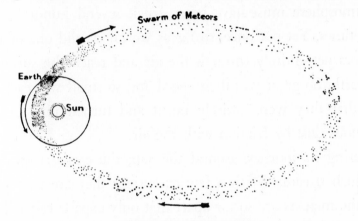

A SWARM OF METEORS

Figure 60. Like hornets, millions and millions of meteors follow long oval paths around the sun. As the earth makes its annual journey in its nearly circular orbit, it is frequently stung by these celestial insects. You can see from the diagram that sometimes the meteors are more numerous in one part of their orbit than in another. Also, sometimes the earth will go around its small circular orbit many times, while the meteors are traveling once around the sun in their long oval path. So it happens that when the earth each year crosses one of these meteor paths, it doesn't always meet the thick swarm of meteors which are more or less bunched together. In the diagram, the earth is passing through the densest part of the swarm of meteors. (From a diagram in *The Outline of Science,* edited by J. Arthur Thomson, published by G. P. Putnam's Sons, New York, 1922. Courtesy of G. P. Putnam's Sons.)

other during a severe hailstorm. The buildings are separated by a narrow alley. As you run from one building to another you are pelted by the hailstones. Naturally, the hailstones hit you from only one direction, that is, the direction from which the wind is blowing. In 1833, the earth, at the rate of almost 20 miles per second, dashed through a stream of meteors, which perhaps in size were not so very different from hailstones. During the earth's brief exposure to this bombardment, its atmosphere must have been struck several hundred thousand times. Yet not once, so far as we know, did one of these meteors get entirely through the air and reach the surface of the earth. So great was their speed and so small was each meteor that they were entirely burnt and turned into gas and luminous dust by friction with the air.

During its journey around the sun, the earth crosses over 500 such streams. With a few exceptions they are very feeble and the meteors are so far apart that only experts can tell that a shower is taking place.

In a first-class shower it is obvious that the meteors appear to come from a single point in the sky. In 1833, and again in 1866, this point was in the constellation of the Lion (Figure 63). Of course, in reality, the meteors are traveling through space in parallel lines. If they appear to come from a point, it is an illusion. A straight railroad track gives you the same illusion. The tracks appear to meet in the distance, yet you know that they are parallel lines.

The earth doesn't always encounter a swarm of shooting stars every time it crosses one of these orbits in its annual trip around the sun. Sometimes the old original comet has not been evenly distributed throughout its orbit, and we then encounter

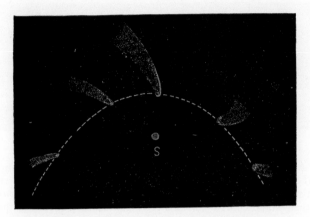

HOW A COMET HANDLES HIS TAIL

Figure 61. That white circle marked S represents the sun. The path the comet follows is marked by the dotted line. In fact you can see the comet in five different positions as it traveled past the sun. You will notice that the tail always points away from the sun. It behaves as smoke would if the sun were blowing wind away from itself in all directions. In this picture the comet is moving from left to right; so the tail is a little curved just as it would be if it were smoke, and the wind from the sun were strong, and the comet were going rapidly. Of course the tail of the comet is not smoke and there is no air and no wind. This picture merely illustrates the repulsive power of sunlight on individual atoms of gas which come from the comet's head. (From a diagram in *Astronomy,* by Russell, Dugan and Stewart, published by Ginn & Co. Courtesy of Ginn & Co.)

HALLEY'S COMET IN 1910

Figure 62. After the appearance of this brilliant comet in 1682, Edmund Halley computed the path in which it was moving, and proved that certain comets mentioned in history were earlier appearances of this one. Halley also predicted that the next return would be in 1759. This prediction came true. It was the first time that a comet had been proved to be moving around the sun in an oval path. Also, it was the first time that the return of a comet had been predicted.

On account of many curious superstitions, people for ages had been terrified by comets. One man thought they were traveling hells to which the spirits of the damned were sent, and they usually were associated with pestilence and calamity. An excellent account of these superstitions is given in the *Great Astronomers,* by H. S. Williams (Simon and Schuster, 1930). Halley effectually destroyed superstitions connected with comets, but, of course, left as many others. Even today we take barbaric joy in shuddering at the number 13, Friday, and an over-turned saltcellar.

We have records of the appearance of Halley's comet on the following dates: 1910, 1835, 1759, 1682, 1607, 1531, 1456, 1145, 1066, 684. Thus, to a greater or less degree, sixteen periods of approximately 75 years each have been recorded. In 1066, the comet was associated with the conquest of England, and in 1456 with the conquest of Constantinople. (From a photograph taken on May 7, 1910, at Santiago, Chile, by the staff of the Lick Observatory. Courtesy of the Lick Observatory.)

many shooting stars on one occasion and few on another. It is much like crossing that narrow alley between those large buildings. If we made the circuit of those buildings once a week and crossed that alley, we would not always encounter a hail-

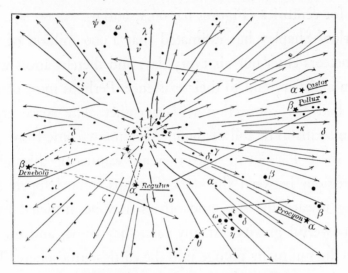

THE LION HURLS STARS AT THE EARTH

Figure 63. Since the shooting stars are coming toward the earth in straight lines, they make a "vanishing point" in the sky. The two rails of a long straight railroad track make a similar vanishing point near the horizon. This is a map of the great shower of Leonids as they radiated from the constellation of the Lion on Nov. 13, 1866. Their previous bombardment of the earth was in 1833. (From a diagram in *Astronomy,* by Russell, Dugan and Stewart; Ginn & Co., publishers. Courtesy of Ginn & Co.)

storm. Some hailstorms would pass down the alley, either before or after we crossed. We might be entirely ignorant of their existence. On the other hand, one hailstorm might appear at regular intervals so that we would become pelted with ice at every third crossing. Those meteors, which apparently come from the direction of the constellation of the Lion, are

95

so distributed in their path that they bombard the earth every 33 years. According to historical records, they have been doing this for centuries. Their next appearance will be in or about 1932. Also, Halley's comet has been observed on successive returns, for centuries (Figures 62, 66A, 66B).

Harlow Shapley has estimated that 1,000 million of these tiny meteors enter our air every day, and thereby meet with a sudden and fiery end to their existence. Perhaps most of them never had any connection with a comet. The space around the sun seems to be full of them. Also, many come from interstellar space. Far out in space they are wandering through the dark regions between the stars. Perhaps some happen to be moving toward the sun, and others may be attracted by the sun's powerful gravity. At any rate, they come, and on their way to the sun many plunge into the earth's atmosphere. These visitors have a velocity, when we see them, of over 40 miles a second. It is because of this great speed that we know they must have originated far out in the depths of space (Figure 64).

Then there are large meteors which crash through the air to the earth (Figure 65). It was one of these, in this case made mostly of iron, which fell from the sky and made that crater three-quarters of a mile wide in Arizona (Figure 51). They also, as far as we know, have no connection with comets. Fortunately for us, these big fellows are few and far between.

96

A DANGEROUS METEOR

Figure 64. This picture represents a meteor which may crash through the air and explode. Such a meteor sometimes reaches the surface of the earth and explodes like a high explosive shell. (From a drawing in *Marvels of the Universe,* part 27, by Arthur Twidle; published by Hutchinson & Co., Ltd. Courtesy of Hutchinson & Co., Ltd.)

A METEOR WHICH FELL IN OREGON

Figure 65. Those little boys didn't come with the meteor. They climbed up to have their photograph taken after the meteor, which weighs more than 15 tons, had been placed in the American Museum of Natural History. Since the meteor struck the earth it has had a hard life, and now is somewhat the worse for wear, as you can see. Probably for many centuries to come it will lead a very sheltered life in the Museum. Let us hope that none of its former associates in the sky will try to find it. (Meteorite from Willamette, Oregon, photographed by J. Kirschmer, American Museum of Natural History of New York City. Courtesy of the American Museum of Natural History.)

Figure 66A. *Upper.* A Very Old Astronomical Drawing. In A.D. 684, the *Nuremberg Chronicle* recorded the appearance of a bright comet which we now know was the famous Halley's comet. By this 8-pointed star the artist may have meant that the head of the comet was very brilliant. (Courtesy of the Yerkes Observatory.)

Figure 66B. *Lower.* Halley's Comet and the Norman Conquest. This is not a celestial jellyfish which these men are looking at. It is a picture, embroidered on linen, of a brilliant comet which appeared in 1066, during the conquest of England. It is part of the famous "Bayeux tapestry" made by order of Odo, bishop of Bayeux, to record William the Conqueror's exploits. We now know that this was one of the many appearances of Halley's comet. (Courtesy of the Yerkes Observatory.)

XVI: MEASURING SPACE

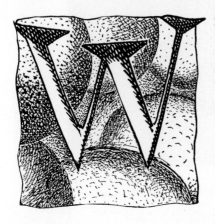

WE ALL know that the farther off a light is the fainter it appears to be. In some respects, light behaves like waves on a pond when you throw in a stone. The waves make a series of circles around the place where the stone fell. The waves travel away from the place in all directions on the surface of the water. Each wave is a ring and the ring grows fainter as it grows larger, until finally it almost disappears. The wave grows fainter because there was only a limited amount of energy in the original splash. That energy had to be spread out over a greater and greater ring as the wave traveled across the pond. Naturally, the wave grew fainter until it disappeared from sight and could have been discovered only by some very delicate instrument.

When you light a candle, the light travels in all directions. It doesn't merely travel north, east, south, and west as did the wave on the pond. It travels up and down as well. Instead of sending out an ever-growing circle, it is sending out an ever-growing sphere. This makes the light grow fainter, the farther it goes from the candle, much faster than did the circular wave. The reason is that the original light from that candle must cover the entire surface of the imaginary ball which surrounds it. Since the imaginary ball keeps growing larger as the light travels farther and farther away, the amount of surface which must be covered by the original energy of that candle is so great that at any one place it soon becomes too faint to affect our eyes, and so we say the candle is "out of sight" or "not visible." Of course, if we used a spyglass we still could see the candle just as we could measure with a delicate instrument that wave on the pond long after we had ceased to see it.

The reason why a light appears fainter the farther off it may be, is very useful to us all. We know, for example, that the headlights of an automobile are very bright. Each light is as bright as many lighted candles. If it is as bright as 200 candles, then we say it is 200 candle power. If we see an automobile light in the distance and it looks faint, we know that the car must be a long way off. You can imagine that some wise man could compare such a distant 200 candle-power lamp with a lighted candle, and tell you just how far away that automobile might be. Of course he could do that only if he knew the candle power of the distant lamp—that is, the real brightness compared with the little candle which he had near by.

That same wise man might say that he could do the same thing with the stars, if he only knew their candle power.

MEASURING SPACE

Since the stars are suns like our sun, it seems absurd to compare them with candles. Let us take something more nearly their own size; let us compare them with the sun. Our job then is to find out whether some star is twice as bright as the sun or only half as bright, or some other known degree of brightness. Then our wise friend, who plays with automobile lights, can tell us how far off the star is.

It would seem as if our job were hopeless, but it isn't. We actually know the sun power of some of the stars because of a discovery made by Miss Leavitt of the Harvard College Observatory.

We see the familiar stars like the Dipper, the North Star, and the Pleiades, and we think they are always the same; always of the same brightness and in the same position. If we do, we are wrong. Thousands of stars change their brightness in a short time, and by very considerable amounts. But some stars change in brightness very slowly and in thousands of millions of years. Also, the stars are continually changing their positions. Very slowly, to be sure, so that with the naked eye we do not notice any change from night to night, or even during our lifetime. Yet the early Americans, who perhaps followed the retreating glacier some 30,000 years ago, would notice quite a change if they could now look at the constellations of the scorpion (Scorpio), and Orion, and the bull (Taurus).

MEASURING SPACE

Just at present we are interested in the stars which change in brightness. Certain of these stars change in brightness with amazing regularity. Sometimes in a few hours they will go from bright to faint and back to bright again. Others will take a week or ten days. These stars are called Cepheid variables, because the first star of this class to be discovered was in the constellation of Cepheus.

What makes the light from some of the stars variable is not thoroughly understood, but due to Miss Leavitt, and later to Harlow Shapley, then at the Mt. Wilson Observatory, we do know a very queer thing about them. The longer the star takes to change from one time of full brightness to the next, the greater is the star's candle power or sun power.

For example, if such a variable star takes 100 days to change from bright to faint to bright again, it is about 22,000 times as bright as the sun, that is, it is giving out 22,000 times more light than the sun. On the other hand, if a Cepheid variable has only about five days between successive bursts of light, then it is only about 700 times as bright as our sun.

Our wise man would at once say that this is like the old problem of the automobile lamp. To find the candle power, or better the sun power, of a Cepheid variable star, we have merely to count the days or hours between successive bursts of light. If the time is long, the star is really very bright; if the time is short, the star is not so bright.

MEASURING SPACE

Our man who was wise about automobile lights can now be wise about Cepheid variable stars; for he now knows their candle power or sun power. Thus he can tell us how far off they must be in order to appear so faint to us.

Cepheid variables are very much like flashing lighthouses, according to E. S. Eddington. You know most lighthouses send out various long and short flashes, so that a sea captain can tell the name of the lighthouse by counting the number of long and short flashes. When he knows the name he can look up the candle power of the lighthouse. In this way he can tell to some extent how far off the lighthouse is. If the captain counts two long flashes and one short one, he can find from his records that the lighthouse is on a certain rock and is 100,000 candle power. Perhaps to the captain it looks very faint on the distant horizon. He might say: "That lighthouse is really very bright; it is 10,000 times brighter than that lantern which is hung up on the mast. Yet the lighthouse and the lantern seem to me to be about the same brightness. Therefore that lighthouse must be about six miles away."

So these Cepheid variables are sending their messages to the astronomer, just as the revolving lighthouses are sending their names and candle powers to the captain. The astronomer can tell how much farther away the Cepheid variable is than the sun, just as the captain can tell how much farther away the lighthouse is than the lantern on the mast.

Thus the Cepheid variables are the flashing lighthouses of the universe. By them we can tell how far we can go in the Milky Way before we come to the dark outer space.

We already have discovered that we are living in a star cluster. You remember that if we use large enough telescopes we will look beyond the stars which make the Milky Way, out into the enormous spaces which separate us from the "island universes."

Now by the help of the Cepheid variables, we can tell how far we must go in each direction before we reach this space which is so empty of stars. It has been shown in the first place that our cluster called the Galaxy is shaped like a watch and really is a collection of huge flattened star clusters. We are about halfway from the edge to the center. When we look out toward the edge in all directions, we see a vast number of stars, which we call the Milky Way. On the other hand, if we look through the thinnest part of the cluster, we see only a comparatively few stars, as, for example, in the direction of the Dipper in the constellation of Ursa Major, the Great Bear, or in the direction of the lion, Leo.

Imagine a long, narrow grove of trees. You walk halfway across this stretch of trees and then stop and look around. In either direction, before you and behind you, only a short distance separates you from the fields in which only a few trees are growing. Of course you see these fields through the trees which are surrounding you. Since the grove is long and narrow only a few trees obscure your view, if you look through the narrowest part.

As you turn and look more and more lengthwise through the grove of trees, you see less and less of the wheat fields. You are looking through so many trees that your view of the wheat fields is becoming more and more obscured. If every tree held a lantern you would say that as you looked through the longest part of the grove you saw a miniature Milky Way.

This watch-shaped star cluster is enormous. Thanks to the Cepheid variables we know its diameter. It would take too much room on this page if we wrote its length in miles. So let us think about it in light-years. The diameter is 250 thousand light-years. In thickness our galaxy is much less than that, perhaps 50 thousand light-years.

Such a vast space seems inconceivable. The sun, an ordinary star, is about halfway from the edge to the center. The sun should not feel lonely; it is estimated by Harlow Shapley, the director of the Astronomical Observatory of Harvard College, that it has 100,000 million companions in this galaxy which we call our Milky Way.

Later we will learn that this giant galaxy is in reality a group of star clusters—a flattened group of galaxies. It is called a "super-galaxy." There are others in space and others still in process of formation. These galaxies are the "island universes."

XVII: SOUND

HERE are tiny waves in the air and we call them sound waves; for sound is not solid, it has no weight, it is really only wave motion.

Waves in the water take time to travel. You can see them move rather slowly across a pond. Sound waves also take time to travel. They are waves which are usually in the air.

A sharp disturbance like a blow will send a sound wave through the air. If it comes all the way to you, it will make the drum of your ear vibrate. This causes a sensation in your ear which you call sound. When you have this sensation you know that something somewhere has struck the air a sharp blow—has made a noise.

Perhaps that sound came from just one stroke of a hammer. One blow sent one wave through the air to your ear. If the hammer is made to strike rapidly, a series of sound waves will be sent out. Now a curious thing will happen. If you strike with that hammer still faster so that the blows are coming at the rate of 25, 30, or 50 per second, your nerves cannot work fast enough to record them as individual waves. They just send word up to the brain that the sound waves are beating against the eardrum in a perfect roar. You call this confusion a tone. If only 50 or 100 waves were striking your ear in one second, you would say you heard a very low tone.

The more waves per second, the higher would be the tone or pitch. But now the eardrum is getting tired and there is a limit beyond which the drum will not respond. That limit is about 20,000 waves per second. Most eardrums positively refuse to work when more than that number of waves enter the ear in a second.

Our ears certainly play us queer tricks with our hearing. When those sound waves are less than 20 per second, we hear them as a rule as individual beats or noises. There is a slight difference among people, and some may hear 18 blows per second as a very low tone. As the number of blows become exceedingly rapid, the nerves tell us the note is of a higher and higher pitch. Finally, at about 20,000 it is extremely shrill. Then all is silence, although the disturbance, whatever it may be, is sending out waves in still greater numbers. There is silence merely because the drum of your ear has "lain down on the job" and refused to vibrate at such an outlandish rate.

In ability to hear high notes, people differ as much as they do with low notes. The chirp of some crickets is a disagreeably piercing note to some and perfect silence to others. To sound waves much beyond 20,000 per second all human ears are deaf.

Like every wave with which we are familiar, sound waves take time to travel. We have all probably seen a man at a distance driving a stake with a sledge hammer and we have been surprised to see the hammer hit the stake an appreciable moment of time before we heard the sound. If the man were 350 yards away, that interval would be about one second, a very noticeable amount of time.

Sometimes fire alarm bells are sounded simultaneously by some electrical device from different towers in a town. However, the sounds by no means reach your ear simultaneously. The sound waves from the more distant towers may reach you several seconds after you have heard the first stroke of the alarm from the nearest bell, for sound takes about 5 seconds to travel one mile. When you hear a bell which you know is two miles away, you may be sure that the bell started ringing about 10 seconds before you heard it.

A thunderstorm gives us the most spectacular example of the speed of sound. A flash of lightning hits the air with a series of sharp blows and at once a set of strong sound waves is broadcasted over the surrounding country. Because these waves usually start high in the air where there is nothing to interfere with their motion, and because they are very intense, we can hear them for several miles. When they reach our ears, we call them thunder.

SOUND

If the flash of lightning were 3 miles away, the thunder would not be heard for about 15 seconds. On the other hand, if the lightning "struck" very near at hand, the flash and the sound would reach you almost at the same moment.

As a thunderstorm approaches usually from the west, the intervals between the flashes and the corresponding peals of thunder grow shorter and shorter and, when the storm passes and disappears in an easterly direction, the number of seconds between the flash and the sound grows larger.

There are some exceptions to this rule, because a thunderstorm is a long ribbon of cloud which stretches usually in a northerly and southerly direction. Therefore, when the cloud is overhead and you are in the very midst of the storm, some flashes of lightning may be near by, while others may be several miles either to the north or south.

Sometimes a distant explosion can be seen for a great many miles, as when a powder factory blows up. If the factory is 12 miles away and you are so placed that you can see the flash when the explosion occurs, then it would be one minute approximately before you heard the noise.

Some explosions have been heard when they were many times farther off than 12 miles. Occasionally, the explosion of a shooting star can be both seen and heard. On such occasions several minutes may elapse between the flash and the sound.

108

XVIII: LIGHT

E ARE going to confess right here that we don't know what light is.

Our ancestors three centuries ago thought light and heat consisted of little pellets which darted out in straight lines from a flame. They were so tiny as to be almost beyond imagination. Without hurting the eyes they just went right in and made our grandparents think that they saw the flame which the little pellets had just left. Of course, if too many entered our grandfathers' eyes, they would say the flame was so bright that it dazzled them. Sir Isaac Newton believed this, and as we soon shall see, he was nearly right.

Also, light behaves as if it were waves like sound. Waves of what?—you might very naturally ask; for you know light comes to us from the sun through more than 90 million miles of nearly empty space. How can we have waves of empty space, waves of nothing? Yet light certainly does behave sometimes like waves, very short, tiny waves.

Thus light behaves in two different ways at the same time

LIGHT

—like waves and like snowflakes driven in a storm. It isn't that light sometimes behaves like waves and at other times like snowflakes. It is more mysterious than even this; for it can behave like waves and like snowflakes both at the same time. Since no one can solve this puzzle, we will sometimes call light a series of waves, and at other times we will speak of it as consisting of tiny bullets of energy, which sometimes are called "quanta" or "photons." Also, we will not be embarrassed because we have made contradictory statements, for this is one of the many problems which are not solved. When we meet with two things which are mutually contradictory, and which are beyond our ability to harmonize, it is better to acknowledge it. We can say to ourselves we simply don't understand, but we hope that some day our researches will help us to understand a little better. This is a much more satisfactory attitude than to imagine an answer which is hardly better than a dream.

By a somewhat complicated but very ingenious method in the laboratory, it has been discovered that apparently the only difference between the violet and red colors is in the number of microscopic waves of light which enter your eyes in a second. If these waves are extremely close together so that 756 millions of millions of them enter your eyes in a second, your nerves are affected in a certain way and you call that sensation violet. These waves are so small they cannot even be seen in a microscope. If you could see what is going on, and if you laid down a foot rule in a beam of violet light, you would find that it took about 62,000 of its waves to cover the space of one inch. That you will ever see one of these waves seems hopeless.

The number of waves per inch in each color in the rainbow has been counted in the laboratory. To give us the sensation we call blue, there must be about 55,000 waves to the inch; green, 48,000; yellow, 44,000; and red, 38,000. The very deepest red is about 33,000. When the waves become so long that less than about 33,000 of them make an inch, our eyes are unable to see them. They make no impression at all upon the nerves of our eyes, so that, for example, an alcohol flame which does send out such waves, and such waves only, is under certain conditions almost invisible.

There also is invisible light at the other end of this series of colors, for there are many waves which are so short and so crowded together that they are unable to give our eyes any sensation at all. They are like those piercing shrieks of some laboratory apparatus, or some insects which are so shrill that they don't affect the drums of our ears. If waves are so short that it takes over 66,000 of them to make an inch, they are totally invisible to our eyes and are called ultra-violet waves.

From the sun we get beams of all the colors in a grand mixture, which we call white. The ultra-violet waves which come from the sun are, of course, invisible. Yet ultra-violet waves have a very remarkable effect upon us. If we are exposed to only a few of these rays they are beneficial—they are the health-giving rays which are so much sought after. Recently, lamps have been made which produce these invisible rays in concentrated form. These very powerful rays are nearly all absorbed by groups of oxygen atoms called "ozone," a layer of atmosphere beginning about 30 miles above the earth's surface. Also, most air contains minute quantities of ozone. However, only a small fraction of these waves gets through to the earth. Too many ultra-violet waves would have a very bad effect upon us.

For several centuries men and women have known how to break up white light into colors by means of a prism, a three-sided piece of glass. It was in 1672 that Sir Isaac Newton established a firm foundation for the modern analysis of color. Raindrops and sunlight have made color from time immemorial, for the Piltdown man of England, who lived perhaps a million years ago, must have seen the rainbows as clearly as we see them. If we are going to use colors as we did the Cepheid variables, to discover some more secrets of the universe, we should be able to lay a sunbeam out in the laboratory and arrange all its colors according to the size of the light waves (Figure 67A).

This can be done by letting the light pass through a prism. Then that beam of light is spread out into a band of color, an artificial rainbow called a spectrum. If you let light go through several prisms and then through a magnifying glass, you can make a very long spectrum. The colors then are spread out in a long band so that sometimes each color is a foot or more in length. Just as in the rainbow, the colors are not sharply divided. Red merges very gradually into yellow, which almost imperceptibly becomes green. Violet occupies nearly half the spectrum. On the other hand, yellow and blue are hardly more than narrow lines crowded between their big neighbors, red, green, and violet.

Such is the spectrum, the artificial rainbow, of a white-hot solid, as, for example, the filament of an electric bulb or a white-hot coal. When such light is passed through a prism, all the colors are always represented and in the positions in which we have just found them. But when we let the light of a very hot (incandescent) gas pass through a prism and then examine it through a magnifying glass, we find a very different situation.

As a rule, only a few colors are represented in the spectrum of a gas. A gas spectrum consists of bright lines of color. Each gas has its own peculiar group of colored lines (Figure 67B). Some gases have only a few and some have thousands of lines of color. They are the "fingerprints" of a gas. When you see a certain group of colored lines in a spectrum, you know you are examining the light from a certain incandescent gas. These colored lines, grouped in such a fantastic manner, are like the

113

combinations of a lock. When you know the meaning of each group, you can unlock the secrets of some distant flame which you might have great difficulty in analyzing in any other way. Each substance has its own group of color lines. Perhaps you wonder how each can be made to give light like a flame. If iron or nickel be placed in an electric arc, it will be turned to vapor or gas. The hot gas will give off light and this light will always show peculiar groups of colored lines which are characteristic of that substance.

We can consider the spectrum of an incandescent solid, like the filament of an electric lamp where all the colors are present, as consisting of an almost infinite number of fine colored lines, placed so close together that they give the appearance of a continuous band of gradually changing color (Figure 67A). Each one of these minute color lines has its own number of waves per inch. When we said that it took about 62,000 waves of violet light to make one inch, we referred to only the middle of that part of the spectrum that we call violet. From the blue band to the end of the violet there is a range of from about 58,000 waves to the inch to about 66,000 waves. If we assume each line of color to have its own special length of wave, then there must be 8,000 lines between the blue and the end of the violet. Our eyes are so crude that we call all these lines violet, although each must differ from its neighbor by a minute amount of color.

The gases are more precise. They give us a few single lines —a few beams of pure color.

Not only is light essential to our lives, but also it is becoming increasingly essential to the study of the whole world in which we live. It is useful partly because its behavior is so remarkable, and it is fascinating because it is so mysterious. From time to time we will find that we are always using some newly discovered characteristic of light with which to discover more of the well-hidden secrets of the universe. Now we come to another very useful trait of light.

Sodium is a common metallic element. It is found in some of our most widely distributed substances such as salt, which is sodium combined with chlorine. When sodium gas is made incandescent by burning sodium in a flame, the spectrum consists for the most part of two bright yellow lines. These two yellow lines are characteristic of sodium gas. If you examine the light of any flame by means of a prism and find these two bright yellow lines, you may be very sure that the flame contains sodium. This is especially useful if the flame is beyond your reach.

The colors of the spectrum are bountiful in their gifts to us. Not only will they tell us what gases are burning in distant flames, but they also will give us the names of gases which surround the stars. Here on the earth the air is our atmosphere. The atmosphere of the sun is very large and exceedingly hot.

LIGHT

Yet we know the names of 62 of its gases for the following reason.

If we let the light from an incandescent solid pass through the hot vapor of iron in an electric arc and then if we examine that light by prisms and magnifying glasses, we will find that the continuous band of color which we expect from an incandescent solid, is crossed by numerous little black lines.

Evidently the iron vapor has destroyed or taken unto itself certain lines of color. This is interesting, but it becomes almost exciting when it is noticed that these dark lines are in the same exact position as the iron's own characteristic color lines. It is apparent then that the iron gas has absorbed and destroyed those very minute shades of color by which iron shines when it is turned into gas by heat. This certainly is a peculiar characteristic and an important one, as we shall be reminded over and over again.

We can see this slaughter of color beams on a large scale by looking at the sun by means of prisms and lenses. A vast array of colors leave the sun every second and shoot through 90 million miles of space to the earth. During the 8 minutes which this journey requires, life for the many color beams is uneventful. However, the moment they reach our atmosphere, the oxygen and water vapor of our air begin their deadly work. They will destroy from sunlight many colors. This accounts for some of the dark lines which we see in the sun's spectrum.

116

THE SPECTRUM

Figure 67. The upper band of color is the spectrum of an incandescent solid. All the visible colors are here arranged in the order of their wave length. It is the laboratory copy of the rainbow. The lower band of colors is the spectrum of a gas. Each gas has its own peculiar group of colored bands. (From Energy: Radiation and Atomic Structure by H. B. Lemon, published in *The Nature of the World and of Man*; The University of Chicago Press. Courtesy of the University of Chicago Press.

THERE IS HYDROGEN IN THIS STAR'S ATMOSPHERE

Figure 68. By means of the great telescope 5 feet in diameter at the Mt. Wilson Observatory the beam of white light from a star called Alpha Pegasi was spread out in a spectrum. Those dark lines mean that hydrogen gas is in the star's atmosphere. (From a photograph of the prismatic spectrum of Alpha Pegasi—type Ao—taken at the Mt. Wilson Observatory with the 60 inch telescope. The spectrum was colored by Mrs. Alice Howard Park under the direction of Alfred H. Joy. Courtesy of the Mt. Wilson Observatory.)

The sun's light would be fairly fortunate if it suffered only those losses which are inflicted by the gases of our air, oxygen, water vapor, and others. The sun has an atmosphere, too, which must be reckoned with. In the sun's atmosphere there are gases of almost every kind—62 have been identified. Some things which we usually think of as hard, like iron, are on the sun not only melted, but actually turned to gas by the tremendous heat. We find in the sun's atmosphere gases of iron, aluminum, tin, and lead. By this means we know the atmosphere of the sun contains gases of the following substances: hydrogen, helium, carbon, oxygen, sodium, magnesium, aluminum, silicon, potassium, calcium, manganese, iron, nickel, cobalt, copper, zinc, silver, tin, lead, and 42 others.[1]

In the atmosphere surrounding the stars we find hydrogen, iron, helium, calcium, and many other gases. The spectrum would be a smooth band of color if it were not for the star's atmosphere of gases. As in the sun, these gases absorb the color beams which they themselves would emit, if they were shining by their own light. Hence, the star spectra are covered with fine dark lines which spell by their peculiar code the names of the gases in their atmospheres (Figure 68).

[1] *Revision of Rowland's Table,* by St. John, Moore, Ware, Adams, and Babcock, published by the Carnegie Institution as Publ. No. 396, 1928.

XIX: WHAT
THE SPECTRUM TELLS US

INCE we have found that sound is a series of waves, let us consider what would happen if the source of the sound were moving rapidly through the air. Perhaps you have watched one of those funny little bugs which swim on the surface of quiet pools of water. You probably have noticed that they send out little ripples on the water and that those minute waves are closer together in front of the bug than they are at his sides or behind him. That is what you would expect to find, for after that bug splashed and sent out the circular ripple, he then rushed toward the receding wave and made another splash. So in front of the bug that second circular wave would be very close to the first one. But behind the bug the two waves would be some distance apart. In other words, the waves caused by a moving body are crowded in front and more widely separated in the rear.

If this is true of sound waves, we would expect the whistle of a locomotive to have a higher pitch when it was approaching us, and a lower pitch the moment it had passed and was receding from us. Such a change in pitch is exactly what does happen. This phenomenon is particularly noticeable if your train is moving and a locomotive whistles as it passes you in the opposite direction. It is conceivable that if you knew the real pitch of the whistle you might be able to tell how fast the locomotive was approaching by noting how much higher in pitch the whistle sounded.

If crowding of the waves applies to bugs and locomotives, why shouldn't it apply to a moving light? If the light waves from the headlight of a locomotive are crowded together as the express train approaches you, why shouldn't the light become a little violet in tinge? Or, perhaps, at least a little bluish? So far as our experience with express trains goes, the headlight doesn't behave in this manner at all. Those light waves really are crowded; but there is a vast difference between the speed of light and the speed of an express train. In a second, light goes 186,000 miles, while even a very fast train will only go about one-fiftieth of a mile in that time. Like the bug and the whistle, the headlight tries to overtake the waves of light which it has just emitted. The headlight has sent out a sphere of light, and in one second that rapidly expanding sphere of particles of light energy has gone 186,000 miles. It has moved with more than explosive violence. During that second the headlight has moved only one-fiftieth of a mile toward one section of that fleeting wave front. When the headlight releases a second wave, it has caused the two waves to be crowded together by less than a millionth of their true distance. As a matter of fact, the two waves would be crowded together by only one nine-millionth of their normal distance from each other. Our eyes could not possibly distinguish such a slight variation in normal wave length. It can only be detected by refined measurements with modern powerful instruments.

The bug could run over the surface of his pool almost as fast as the ripples which he caused. No wonder that he could crowd them before him. The express train carried that whistle toward you by 100 feet per second, or about 70 miles per hour. This is almost a tenth as fast as sound travels, for sound moves through the air at about 1,100 feet per second, or 750 miles per hour. If the whistle tried to catch the sound waves it would be hopelessly outrun. Yet the whistle could go fast enough to crowd those sound waves perceptibly, for you noticed that the pitch of the whistle was decidedly higher when the train was rushing toward you.

Let us hunt for lights which are moving so much faster than locomotive headlights that perhaps even light waves will be noticeably crowded. We already have found that the earth is moving around the sun so fast that it makes an express train look as if it were standing still. The earth moves about 18 miles a second in its yearly journey around the sun. This is much faster than an express train, which only moves about one-fiftieth of a mile per second. It may be then that among the stars we can find velocities so great that we can measure the crowding of the light waves. We could hardly expect a yellow star to become blue as it approached us and crowded its waves, and then red as it receded and left its waves at longer and longer intervals. Such changes would imply that the star was moving nearly half as fast as light. This of course is not the case, and therefore, to notice the crowding of even a star's light waves, we must find some very delicate method of measurement.

We have noticed that the color beams, which are characteristic of each gas, appear as very fine sharp lines whose positions can be accurately measured. Also the dark lines, which take the place of those color beams under certain conditions, are very fine and sharply defined. Therefore, if a moving star approached us rapidly we might expect to be able to notice a slight change in the position of these lines.

In 1848, a French astronomer, Fizeau, first described how these measurements might be made. Later, other astronomers selected a star which had in its atmosphere some gas that was well known. For example, it is possible to take a star which has a spectrum which is crossed by the many dark hydrogen lines, and compare its spectrum with that of a tube of hydrogen gas. You can so arrange the spectrum of the star and of the hydrogen gas that they both appear in the telescope side by side. In the star's spectrum there are the dark lines caused by the hydrogen in the star's atmosphere (Figure 68). If the star were standing still, continuous with these dark lines would be the colored lines of the incandescent hydrogen in the tube. However, if the star were moving rapidly toward us the dark hydrogen lines would be moved a little toward the violet end of the spectrum, or, if the star were receding from us, the lines would be moved toward the red. All the while the colored lines from the bright hydrogen tube would be the immovable standard to tell us whether the dark lines were moving toward the violet or toward the red, that is, whether the star was approaching or receding from us.

Light travels 186,000 miles per second, as we have said before. If a star went half as fast, that is 93,000 miles per second, the light waves in front would be crowded to one-half their normal distance apart. A deep red beam of color then would have twice as many waves per inch. Its normal 33,000 waves per inch would be increased to 66,000 waves per inch, but that is the frequency of the very last ray of violet which we can see. Therefore, a star with such a velocity would have its dark lines moved clear across the spectrum. If the star, when it was standing still, was giving off nothing but red rays, that is, waves between 30 and 40 thousand per inch, then, as it approached us at this tremendous speed, it would be of a violet color.

It is unfortunate that we find no such interesting speed among the stars. The displacement of those dark lines, compared with the corresponding colored lines of the bright gas imprisoned in the glass tube, is extremely slight. In 1888, these two sets of lines were photographed for the first time. Now the movement of these lines is always studied by means of photographs which are examined by the help of a microscope. The velocities in miles per second have been found for thousands of stars. Some are coming toward us and some are going from us. Some are moving a few miles per second and some several hundred miles.

Of course this method of research tells us nothing about the movement of a star to the right or left. It merely tells us that the star is approaching or receding, and how fast.

V. M. Slipher of the Lowell Observatory at Flagstaff, Arizona, has examined the distant clusters of stars called island universes by means of prisms, lenses, tubes of gases, and photographic plates. He has found that most of the island universes are moving several hundred miles per second. For some reason not well understood, these island universes appear to be moving away from us. The more distant they are the more rapidly they seem to be running away, according to E. P. Hubble and M. L. Humason of the Mount Wilson Observatory. The very remote ones give the appearance of traveling away at the almost inconceivable rate, for a star cluster, of over 11,000 miles per second. This is probably something like an optical illusion. It is very improbable that the island universes are almost unanimous in their desire to leave us. Also, it seems quite improbable that the farther they go into remote space the greater is their speed.

Like the poor shooting stars which were burnt up in our air, these star clusters must be perfectly unconscious of the speed with which they are rushing toward or from the Milky Way. You may say that because they are masses of gas like our sun and without brains, they naturally don't know where they are going or how fast. Undoubtedly you are right, but it seems at least possible that among the millions of millions of stars in these galaxies there may be a few which have planets like the earth. On some of them there may be intelligent animals who can use prisms, tubes of gas and photographic plates as well as we can. Their astronomers are probably saying:

"There is a very distant star cluster which is flattened and shaped something like a watch. We know how far off it is because we can count the flashes of some of those curious lighthouse variable stars. It would take light many millions of our standard years to reach us from that cluster. But more strange than anything else, it is going away from us at terrific speed, while of course we are standing still in space."

Which is standing still and which is moving? Perhaps we may both be moving.

XX:
TEMPERATURE BY SPECTRUM

OMETIMES we cannot discover the secrets of the world merely by our eyes, ears, and nerves. We have to use what we call a "law" to give us the information. For example, we know that when the mercury in a thermometer rises, the air feels hot, and when it falls the air feels cool. That our feelings should vary with the length of a small column of mercury, at first sight, seems ridiculous. Yet it is a law which we have all found is invariably true.

Perhaps if we hunted we might find another law which would tell us the temperature of a flame. We know that an ordinary glass thermometer would break if we put it in a flame. Wilhelm Wien discovered just such a law which does not require the use of a glass thermometer. It is a very curious law and very different from the law of the rise and fall of a mercury column. By means of a prism Wien spread the light from a hot body into a colored spectrum and then by a very delicate instrument, which for convenience we might call a thermometer, he measured the temperature of each band of color. Also, he measured in this way those invisible colors, the infra-red and ultra-violet. Curiously enough these colors, invisible and visible, weren't all of the same temperature. There always was one point in the spectrum which was the hottest. The interesting thing was that the hotter the object which was giving off the light, the more this hot point in the spectrum moved toward the violet. Thus Wien discovered the law that the position of the hot point in the spectrum can be made to give the temperature of the flame which is making the light.

This law was immediately used to get the temperature of the furnaces in steel mills. Also flames which are inaccessible can have their temperatures determined in this way. A body does not have to be on fire to have its temperature measured by the spectrum; for Wien's law will give you the temperature of red-hot iron. Naturally, astronomers applied this method to some flames into which you cannot place a thermometer, such as those which surround the sun and stars. Then for the first time we knew the surface temperatures of the stars, the planets, the moon, and the sun.

THE SURFACE TEMPERATURES OF A FEW STARS

Gamma of Cassiopeia	30,000°	Fahrenheit
Vega	20,000°	"
North Star	12,000°	"
Capella	10,000°	"
Beta of Andromeda	6,000°	"

XXI: COLOR
AND WHY THE SKY IS BLUE

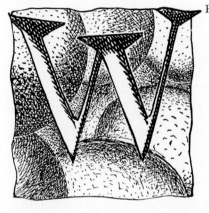

WHEN a beam of white sunlight enters a darkened room and happens to illuminate a painting, we see sometimes many colors—red, green, and violet. Yet when we touch the paint on the picture we find it cold —no incandescent gas; no red-hot coals. That ray of white light has been converted into many brilliant colors by coming in contact with the paint. We know that certain paint, whenever it is illuminated by white light, always will give us those wave lengths which we call red. Other paints will, with the same regularity, always send us waves of light which have the number per inch which we call green, and so on, for a multitude of colors. Here is a mysterious transformation that is taking place before us at every turn. We know something but not all about this secret. As we go on with this story you will probably more and more agree with Edison, who said that we know only one-millionth of one percent of all that can be known. Two hundred years earlier, Sir Isaac Newton compared all knowledge to a huge beach and claimed that he and his fellow men had merely picked up a few interesting pebbles here and there.

When rays of light strike a smooth substance they are reflected just as a billiard ball is reflected when it hits the cushions at the edge of the table. If the substance is very smooth like a polished mirror, nearly all the light is reflected. If the incoming ray is white, then the reflected ray also is white. Or, if the incoming ray is red, the reflected ray is red. On the other hand, if the substance is full of microscopic holes as lampblack is, then almost no light is reflected. We say the incoming white light is absorbed. To a certain extent that is true, but soon the steady stream of energy from the light beam makes the lampblack warm. Then that black surface in its turn sends out waves, but these waves are so far apart that our eyes cannot notice them. We call them heat waves, for they affect our thermometers, and we can feel their warmth by the nerves in our hands. If we passed these rays through a prism we would find they were beyond the deepest red called "infra-red." Of course we couldn't see them. We know they are there in the spectrum because they affect a thermometer, or some other delicate instrument for measuring heat.

The sun has sent down these millions of pellets of energy in serried ranks, as the gusts of wind in a snowstorm marshal countless snowflakes in company formation. Then they charge the rough surface of the lampblack. Their ranks are broken, but

JOSEPH VON FRAUNHOFFER (1787-1826)

Figure 69. Born at Straubing in Bavaria, this German optician and physicist was by profession an instrument maker and manufacturer of lenses. Although the dark lines in the solar spectrum had been discovered in 1802, it was Fraunhoffer who brought them prominently to the attention of scientists in 1814. He also made the first map of the solar spectrum, having measured the positions of over five hundred lines. For these reasons the dark lines in the solar spectrum are frequently called "Fraunhoffer lines." (Reproduced by permission of the University of Chicago Press. Courtesy of the Yerkes Observatory.)

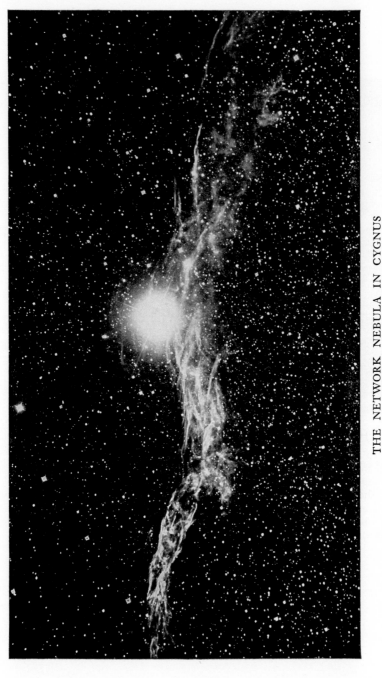

THE NETWORK NEBULA IN CYGNUS

Figure 70. A vast collection of atoms, brilliantly illuminated by neighboring stars. Above there are fewer stars than below, because above there is a thin veil of nebula only faintly illuminated. There are several of these filamentous nebulae which make roughly a loop. Careful measurements show that this loop is growing larger. If we assume that it has been moving in ages past at the present rate, it must have started as a star during the Pleistocene Period. (From a photograph of N.G.C. 6960 taken at the Mt. Wilson Observatory, with the telescope 8 feet in diameter. Exposure 12 hours, July 12, 13, 14, 1915, Southern Part of Network Nebula. Courtesy of the Mt. Wilson Observatory.)

their fighting spirit, their energy, remains. The particles of the lampblack are made to vibrate, which causes a new set of energy waves to be emitted. However, the lampblack does not vibrate fast enough to send out energy waves so close together that they can affect our eyes. They are too far apart even to be called red, so we have named them heat waves. For this reason black clothes are warmer than white clothes, for the white is a better reflector and absorbs much less of the energy of the sun's rays.

Again, a beam of sunlight strikes a partially smooth surface. The sun drives his orderly battalions to the attack as before. The infantry, we will assume, enter the substance and are absorbed. Their energy is transformed into those long heat waves as before. This time, however, the cavalry refuse to enter. They dash off in another direction—they are reflected. Their ranks are so close together that they are known as color-beams of violet light. So when they enter our eyes they give us the sensation of violet. We call the paint which covered that surface violet paint, for we find that it always reflects only those waves of violet frequency and absorbs all others. Thus, an object is colored merely because it reflects certain beams of light to our eyes.

All surfaces are not quite so simple as these two examples. Some material reflects a variety of waves of different lengths. It gives us a blended color which our artists can analyze. They might say that it consisted mostly of reflected red and yellow rays with a very few of the violet. The others were all absorbed and their energy was turned into heat waves. When light becomes heat, we say it is "converted" into heat.

Our atmosphere is full of very minute particles, extremely fine dust. Some of the short blue waves are reflected by these particles. The waves of other lengths pass them by and are little affected. Also the groups of atoms called "molecules" help to scatter the light. A molecule of water vapor consists of two atoms of hydrogen combined with one atom of oxygen. The reflected blue waves bounce from one particle to another until finally they reach our eyes from all over the sky. Hence, we say that the sky is blue; for wherever we look we get this blue sensation. When an aviator goes many thousands of feet into the air, he reports that the sky is darker than as seen from the surface of the earth. That means that he has gotten beyond the dust and most of the water vapor; the air above him is reflecting little light of any color, so it appears to him with much less than its usual brilliance.

When the sun is setting it shines through many miles of dust-laden air. It has lost so many of its blue waves that the red now predominate, and the sun sets as if it were a red ball.

The air extends so far above the ground on which we walk that even the exploring trips of aviators do not go far enough to give us any real knowledge of that great mass of very rare atmosphere which lies for perhaps several hundred miles above our heads. On the surface of the earth such a distance would be

ANOTHER PART OF THE NETWORK NEBULA

Figure 71. There is reason to believe that due to some catastrophe the original star, from which this Network Nebula may have started, exploded and sent out this ever expanding cloud. That accident, if it happened at all, occurred during the last interglacial epoch when Europe and America were warmer than they are now. The Neanderthal men were coming up the valley of the Danube and preparing to conquer Europe and drive out or exterminate the Chellean men and women. (From a photograph of N.G.C. 6960 taken at the Mt. Wilson Observatory, July 2, 3, and 4, 1910, with the telescope 5 feet in diameter. Exposure 10¼ hours. Courtesy of the Mt. Wilson Observatory.)

A NEBULA MADE VISIBLE BY A STAR

Figure 72. If it weren't for the light of this star in the constellation of Auriga we couldn't see this beautiful nebula. It isn't accurate to say that the nebula shines by reflected light. The light is transformed by the nebula and reissued with slightly different wave lengths forming a spectrum of bright lines. It is something like fluorescence. (From a photograph of N.G.C. 1405 taken at the Mt. Wilson Observatory, December 20, 1922, with the telescope 8 feet in diameter. Exposure 2¾ hours. Courtesy of the Mt. Wilson Observatory.)

only a few hours' journey by railroad, yet it seems to be beyond our reach even in an airplane. A serious effort is being made by Dr. Robert H. Goddard of Worcester, Massachusetts, to explore this region. He plans to send up especially constructed rockets to very great heights. These rockets will be equipped with instruments which will be automatically released when they are several tens of miles above the surface of the earth. By means of small parachutes the instruments will come gently down to the ground. These instruments will hold samples of air and self-recording thermometers. Then in our laboratories we can analyze our air and learn a great deal about the distant border of the earth's atmosphere. For one thing, we will know more definitely how very cold it is in those regions beyond the denser blue sky.

Colored glass behaves somewhat as colored paint. It lets waves of a certain number to the inch pass through undisturbed. The other waves are absorbed and ultimately converted into these long waves called heat. If the glass allows only waves which are 35,000 to the inch to pass through, we call it red glass; but if the only waves to get through in their original state are as many as 56,000 to the inch, we say it is blue glass.

XXII: COSMIC CLOUDS

HE Romans called a cloud a "nebula," and we have used that word to describe faint patches of light which we see through a telescope. We already have found by using a large telescope that some of these luminous "clouds" consist in part of stars. You know that on a clear dark night the Milky Way looks as if it were a band of fleecy and luminous clouds, yet in even a small telescope it becomes a mass of sparkling stars. The same thing is true of nebulae, but there is a slight difference. No matter how large the telescope, some nebulae do not become stars (Figures 70 and 71). Apparently they are real clouds. Not clouds of water like our thunderclouds, but clouds of electrons, protons, and atoms, sometimes shining by their own light, sometimes shining by light they have received from neighboring stars. They give the appearance of being illuminated by reflected light; but in reality they absorb and then emit, slightly modified, the light of the near-by stars (Figure 72).

Some of these nebulae are near by, astronomically speaking,

132

THE ORION NEBULA

Figure 73. To the naked eye this nebula is a faint and slightly blurred star. (From a photograph of N.G.C. 1976; Mt. Wilson Observatory; telescope 8 feet in diameter. Courtesy of the Mt. Wilson Observatory.)

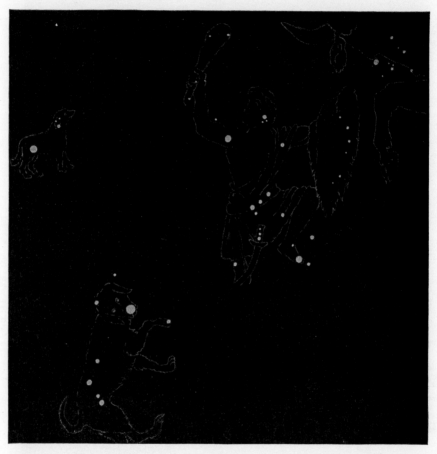

CONSTELLATIONS OF CANIS MAJOR, CANIS MINOR, ORION, AND TAURUS

Figure 74. Slightly modified from drawings in *Atlas Coelestis,* by Eduard Heis, 1872.

and some are the famous island universes. Those near by are within the limits of our own Milky Way galaxy. These neighboring nebulae certainly look like clouds. The two in Cygnus (the constellation of the Swan) look like cirrus clouds (Figures 70 and 71)—those long streams of white cloud which sometimes precede a storm. Then there is the famous Orion nebula surrounding the middle star in the sword of Orion (Figures 73 and 74). It is called θ (Theta) Orionis. In English, that name would be Theta of Orion, who was a famous hunter. In the sky, Orion seems to be tantalizing the bull (Taurus) by holding up a lion's skin; while behind him the unicorn (Camelopardalis) is standing serenely indifferent to the turmoil around him.

At Orion's feet stands his famous hunting dog, Sirius (Canis Major, the big dog) (Figure 74). When Diana gave Orion those acres in the sky for his permanent residence, she little dreamed that underneath the surface there was a vast nebula. Orion, when he discovered it, must have felt like a North American Indian who has found oil under his reservation.

Some parts of the Orion cloud are bright, because it is excited to luminescence by the surrounding stars. The Orion nebula gives bright lines in its spectrum. However, somewhere in the sky between us and the Orion nebula there are dark clouds; at least they look dark to us. Such a one is the famous Dark Bay (Figure 75). If you could fly for years, so far that you would measure your flight in light-years, to the other side of the Dark

133

Bay, you might find that it was after all a fleecy cloud—a luminous nebula. From that other side it may receive a great deal of strong "sunlight" from neighboring stars. Thunderclouds on the earth behave in this way. When you can see the sunlight on a cloud you know what a brilliant mass of fleecy whiteness it becomes. On the other hand, when the cloud of a thunderstorm comes between you and the sun in the afternoon, you can see only the dark side. Then the cloud seems to be a great black mass like the Dark Bay (Figure 75).

Apparently there are many of these clouds of gas which come between us and some of the stars (Figures 76, 77, 78, and 79). We don't know much about them. They are almost incredibly large. It would take light, traveling 186,000 miles a second, many years to go from one end to the other of one of these dark nebulae. If the sun entered such a dark nebula, it might take tens of thousands of years to get out; for the sun is moving among the stars at only about 11 miles per second.

Perhaps a dark nebula consists of individual atoms, or electrons, driven hither and thither by sunlight and starlight. Like dust on a windy day, these stray electrons may be gathered together in clouds. Sometimes these clouds absorb and then emit the starlight and help to make the sky brilliant, and sometimes they obscure the starlight and darken the sky.

Among the stars these dark clouds of atoms and electrons may be known as the smoke nuisance of the galaxy. The cold

A CELESTIAL STORM CLOUD

Figure 75. From the left a dark cloud of atoms and electrons is creeping over the sky. A few stars and nebulae are shining on the left because they are between us and the cloud. Evidently the other side of the cloud is brightly lighted by neighboring stars; for you can see the "silver lining" to even that great black mass which is leading the advance of darkness. (Dark nebula called Barnard 33. From a photograph taken November 19, 1920, at Mt. Wilson Observatory with the Hooker telescope 8 feet in diameter; exposure 3 hours. Courtesy of the Mt. Wilson Observatory.)

LIGHT NEBULA, DARK NEBULA, AND A METEOR

Figure 76. On the left we have an irregular cloud of atoms illuminated by some nearby star. On the right also an irregular cloud of atoms, but if it is illuminated at all it is from the other side. These two pictures are from different parts of the sky, but the nebulae are so much alike in shape that they are interesting. While the photograph of the bright nebula was being taken, a meteor went by and recorded its trail. (Dark nebula in Cepheus photographed by E. E. Barnard, July 15, 1909. The bright nebula is N.G.C. 6992. Photographs taken at the Yerkes Observatory of the University of Chicago, and reproduced by permission of the University of Chicago Press. Courtesy of the Yerkes Observatory.)

iron meteor may look forward to the time when the stars have ceased to hurl parts of themselves—their electrons, protons, and quanta—into space in their mad desire to shine. Then the meteors would say: "We can travel through space without getting ourselves dusty with clouds of electrons and protons. Also, we shan't be bothered any more by those darting quanta, which always are trying to get between an electron and his proton and are pushing the revolving electron into outer paths. Of course we will have to be very careful not to run into one of those dark stars which have cooled off and become cold and black. Still, if we 'watch our step,' we can get along very well, and how nice and clean the galaxy will be!"

When we look at photographs of those illuminated clouds (Figure 76), they look as dense as the smoke from a bonfire. Their appearance is deceiving. In reality they are so light and rare that a whiff of smoke would seem like lead in comparison. They are sometimes called "cosmic clouds." Apparently we see the sun and stars very clearly, yet there is evidence that we are just emerging from a cosmic cloud. It may be a quarter of a million years since the solar system entered this cloud, and it may be several tens of thousands of years before we emerge.

This very fascinating subject has only just begun to be investigated. It is now suspected that cosmic clouds have played a very important part in the history of life on the earth, and they may seriously affect life in the future.

COSMIC CLOUDS

In Chapter XXI we learned how very fine particles in the air can make the sky blue and the sun red at sunset and sunrise. Yet there is so much space between each particle, and each one is so tiny, that they are wholly invisible to the naked eye. On a clear day, in the mountains or on a desert, we look right through these particles and think the air is perfectly transparent.

Sometimes this dust in the air becomes temporarily more dense. Once in a while a volcano is so active that it cannot force all its hot gases, steam and lava through the crater. Then it may explode like a steam boiler, the safety valve of which was too small or was stopped up. The top of the mountain is actually blown away, and with such violence that occasionally a cubic mile of rock and lava is scattered over the land. A vast quantity of such rock is pulverized by the explosion into the finest kind of dust. It is as fine as the particles of smoke, and is blown so far into the air that it is caught by the currents high up in the sky and carried all around the earth. For about a year after one of these explosions, the air is unusually full of dust so that the sun is more red than usual at sunset and sunrise, but the earth is affected in a more important way than by the color of its sunsets. During the year or so that those fine dust particles are floating in the upper strata of our atmosphere, they scatter a certain number of the rays of sunlight and so prevent some of them from reaching the surface of the earth.

You probably are thinking this is very trivial, and that such an ethereal screen of minute particles could have no effect upon our lives. On the other hand, these volcanic dust particles have a considerable effect upon our climate, for the year after one of these terrific explosions we are apt to have an unusually severe winter and a cool summer. After the explosion of the volcano Katmai in Alaska on June 6, 1912, the temperature of the whole world was below normal for the following year. The great eruption of Mont Pelée in Martinique, May 8, 1902, had the same effect. On August 27, 1883, the volcano Krakatoa in the Straits of Sunda near Java, blew off its top in the greatest explosion since 1783. For two or three years the world suffered from unusual cold. Also the sunsets were noticeably more brilliant than usual. The year 1816 was known in America as "the year without a summer." The crops were almost a complete failure. This famine year was preceded by the terrific explosion of Mt. Tomboro, Sunbawa, Dutch East Indies, in April, 1815, which killed 56,000 people, and "blew up so much dust that for 'three days there was darkness at a distance of 300 miles.'" These facts have been taken from a discussion of this subject in *Physics of the Air* by W. J. Humphreys.[1]

Thus we find that fine dust held in suspension in our atmosphere can materially affect our lives, even if such dust is invisible to the naked eye. It is estimated that it would take about 14,000

[1] Professor of meteorological physics, United States Weather Bureau. Published by the Franklin Institute, Philadelphia.

COSMIC CLOUDS

of these particles of volcanic dust, placed side by side, to make one inch. Perhaps you are already asking: "What would happen if a cosmic cloud blew in from interstellar space and enveloped the sun, earth and the whole solar system? Would the sun look redder than usual? Would the cosmic dust scatter enough sunlight so that the earth would be cool, or even cold?" You remember how the blue sky is caused by the blue rays from the sun being scattered by the dust particles in the air. Also we found that when we look at the sun while it is setting, it generally appears to be red, because so many of the blue rays have been scattered far and wide by the dust near the horizon (Chapter XXI). It is, consequently, very proper for us to ask what effect cosmic dust might have on the light and heat which we receive from the sun.

These would be very pertinent questions, and they have been partly answered by Harlan Stetson, director of the Perkins Observatory.[1] Mr. Stetson thinks that we now are in such a cosmic cloud. It may be that the solar corona is that part of the cosmic cloud which is made visible by the blinding light of the sun. The tremendously powerful lines of magnetic force near the sun have warped the particles of dust into long familiar streamers (Figures 1 and 6). In the same way, comets' tails may be the dust particles illuminated by the electrons, protons and quanta driven from the head of the comet by the action of the

[1] *Scientific Monthly,* September, 1930.

STARS OBSCURED BY BOTH DARK AND LIGHT CLOUDS

Figure 77. A nebula will obscure the stars whether it is dark or light. Of course both dark and light nebulae in this case are probably just alike. The dark patches indicate that there is a nebula, which is preventing us from seeing the faint stars. Sometimes these nebulae appear dark because they are not illuminated by any neighboring stars, and sometimes because we are on the nebula's dark side and cannot see the illuminated parts. (Neighborhood of Rho Ophiuchi. Photographed by E. E. Barnard, June 5, 1905, with the Bruce telescope, 10 inches in diameter, exposure 4 hours and 30 minutes; reproduced by permission of the University of Chicago Press. Courtesy of the Yerkes Observatory.)

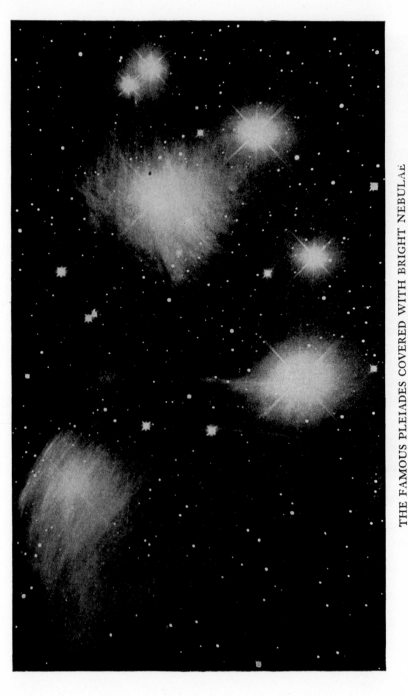

THE FAMOUS PLEIADES COVERED WITH BRIGHT NEBULAE

Figure 78. To the naked eye this cluster is without a trace of either a light or dark nebula. The photographic plate can record fainter light than the human eye can see. Hence, in a long exposure, the stars of the Pleiades are found to be surrounded with nebulosity, which is reflected light from neighboring stars. In this case it is actually reflected light, for the light of the nebula gives the same spectrum as that given by the stars. This is not like those nebulae which absorb the light of neighboring stars and then emit them with slightly altered wave lengths. (From a photograph taken at the Yerkes Observatory, and reproduced by permission of the University of Chicago Press. Courtesy of the Yerkes Observatory.)

sun (Figure 62). These dust particles would not be illuminated like reflected light. They would receive the energy from the comet's head and then impart it to us in a slightly modified form.

To us, our climate is of more importance than solar coronas and comets' tails. We want to know what caused the Great Ice Age, and whether we are approaching another glacial epoch or another unusually warm period. There is some reason to believe that these cosmic dust particles do scatter the sunlight and, if there are enough of them, they might make the earth so cool as to cause an ice age. Perhaps during the last million years or so we went successively through four such clouds, which would account for the four great periods of coldness which afflicted the earth during the Pleistocene period. Apparently we still are in the outskirts of that cloud. Geologists say the fourth and last glacial period of the Pleistocene is only about three-quarters over; for we still have Greenland and the Antarctic continent in perpetual ice. Judging from the past history of the earth, both of these places should be rich in vegetation. So the solar corona and the comets' tails may be the visible cosmic dust cloud which is causing icebergs in the North Atlantic Ocean.

There is some reason to believe that most of this cosmic cloud, which perhaps caused our Great Ice Age of the Pleistocene period, lies in the direction of the constellation of Orion. If all this is so, it is of vital importance to us to know whether we now are approaching a clear space in which the sun's light will reach us undimmed, or whether we are approaching another wisp of cloud which, in 50 thousand years, again will bring an ice sheet a mile thick over parts of North America and Europe. It is not beyond the realm of possibility that further research and larger telescopes may enable us to answer these questions at least in part.

In leaving this subject we must bear in mind that any information concerning a cosmic cloud is only a few decades old. In this part of our map of knowledge we have made only a mere reconnaissance, but from year to year you may learn of new discoveries concerning dark nebulae or cosmic clouds.

MEROPE OF THE PLEIADES

Figure 79. This fleecy nebula, apparently wind blown like a cloud in our blue sky, is the way just one star in the Pleiades looks when it has its photograph taken by a telescope 5 feet in diameter. (N.G.C. 1432. Exposure 5 hours, October 9, 1909, by the 60 inch telescope of the Mt. Wilson Observatory. Courtesy of the Mt. Wilson Observatory.)

A GLOWING BALL OF ENORMOUS SIZE

Figure 80. An early stage in the life of a milky way. (From a photograph of N.G.C. 3379 taken at Mt. Wilson Observatory. Courtesy of the Mt. Wilson Observatory.)

XXIII: THE YOUTH
OF AN ISLAND UNIVERSE

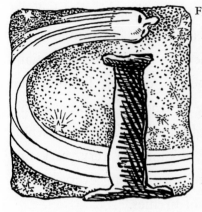 F THAT intelligent meteor who disliked cosmic clouds traveled far beyond our galaxy of stars, he might eventually find he was approaching an island universe. It would take him a long time to get there, for even one of the nearest island universes is a million light-years distant and the most remote ones which we can see are 200 million light-years away. Generally speaking, these island universes are about one or two million light-years apart all through space, except here and there where they have gathered together in clouds. It is estimated that 30 million of them are within the range of the great 100-inch telescope of the Mt. Wilson Observatory.

If the meteor were a scientist, and if he traveled through space for millions of years, and if he always rode a sunbeam at the rate of 186,000 miles a second, then he might classify the island universes. He might take their pictures and arrange them as you would a museum exhibit.

Our scientific meteor did this very thing. He tamed a sunbeam and drove furiously through space and photographed many island universes for us. Occasionally we will let him tell you about them as he told us when he brought these photographs back one by one:

"I found that some of these islands are huge round balls of glowing gas—masses of electrons and atoms, sometimes called globular nebulae (Figure 80). They are shining because many of their atoms are exploding. When I got near, I found that every now and then an electron, instead of running madly around his proton, would fall right into it. Then the whole atom would disappear in a blaze of glory—a very, very tiny blaze, to be sure. Because so many are exploding every second, the great mass shines like millions of fireflies."

Before starting on a second long journey the meteor brushed off all the dust—the electrons and atoms. Then he urged his sunbeam to hurry and run at the rate of 186,000 miles per second. After a long journey in our time, but instantly in his time, he reached the constellation of Virgo (the virgin), and photographed another island.

He was surprised to find that this one was a little flattened (Figure 81), and then he noticed that it was revolving. "It is," he said, "shrinking a little, and the more it shrinks the faster it must revolve, because that is a famous law which was discovered on the earth a long, long time ago. Of course when it revolves, it has to flatten on the top and bulge out at the sides. The old earth did that, too. It flattened at the poles and bulged out at

THE GLOWING BALL FLATTENS AT THE POLES

Figure 81. Spinning on an axis the ball bulges at the equator and enters another stage in the history of a milky way. The second example in the series of photographs selected by Sir James Jeans. (From a photograph of N.G.C. 4621 taken at the Mt. Wilson Observatory. Courtesy of the Mt. Wilson Observatory.)

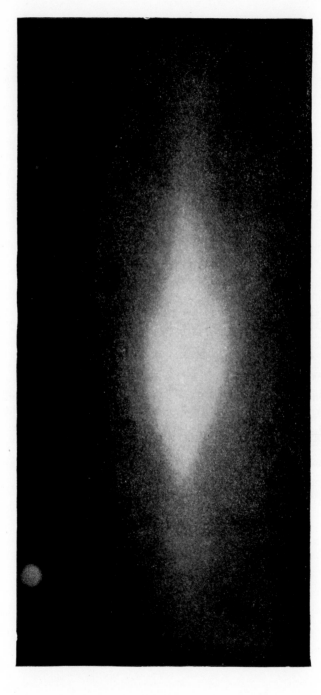

AN EQUATORIAL BULGE BECOMES A RING

Figure 82. As if some celestial blacksmith had hammered the glowing ball in a forge, the bulging at the equator has become a ring of incandescent gas, thousands of millions of miles wide. The third in the Sir James Jeans series. (From a photograph of N.G.C. 3115, constellation of Sextans, taken at the Mt. Wilson Observatory, December 25, 1911, by the telescope 5 feet in diameter. Exposure 1-2/3 hours. Courtesy of the Mt. Wilson Observatory.)

the equator; because it was turning around so fast in order to give night and day to those funny white primates called men and women."

Then the meteor photographed a third island universe, which he found in the southern hemisphere. It was all the more flattened. On the sides, the gas—the atoms and electrons—had begun to squeeze out in a flat disc (Figure 82). It took the meteor a long time as measured by our clocks to get into a good place from which to photograph this island universe, for, although he never dismounted but rode his sunbeam hard, he was more than 100,000 of our years going once around one of these great island universes. Of course for him, since he was riding a sunbeam, time ceased to exist.

It was slow work, but the meteor was persistent. He said that he was going to photograph every stage in the life of an island universe, and so he made a snapshot of a fourth nebula (Figure 83). Here a curious thing was noticed. A black line runs across the nebula at its equator. The meteor felt sad. Was it possible that he again was getting into a smoky atmosphere? Could it be that in its rapid revolving, the nebula had thrown out some of its used-up electrons and atoms and that they had gathered in a huge ring of dust or smoke around this glowing island?

To verify this idea the meteor went to a fifth and very old island (Figure 84). This island was a long way off in the constellation of Coma Berenices (Berenice's hair). It took thousands of our years for his sunbeam to carry him there, and always remember that a sunbeam travels 186,000 miles a second. This figure is an important feature of the world in which we live, for nothing but imagination can travel faster than a sunbeam.

This island, as you can see, he also photographed from the edge, and again he found a ring of dust. In this old nebula the central ball had become smaller, because most of its substance had been driven out into that wide disc of glowing gas by its revolving motion.

At this time a wise old comet came along and told the meteor he had photographed all these nebulae as seen from the edge. Said the comet:

"That shows how the island universes change their shape as they shrink and revolve faster and faster, but the people in the earth museums would like to see how these island nebulae look when you climb up in space so high that you can see the flat side."

The meteor did this. He drove his sunbeam far off to the constellation of Pegasus (the famous horse with wings), and photographed an old and very flat island universe which was revolving rapidly. This photograph is reproduced in Figure 85.

As you might imagine, these islands are very delicate. They started as extremely rarefied gas, but in the course of thousands of millions of years they became, in part at least, masses of stars

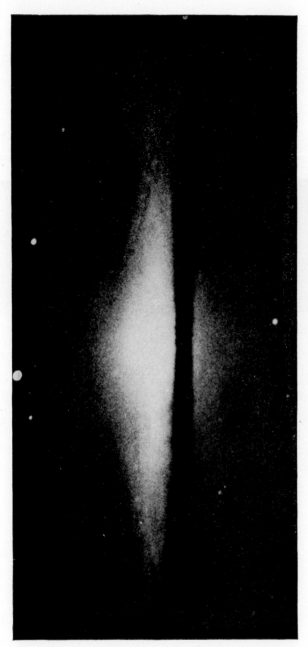

THE GLOWING BALL CREATES A SMOKE SCREEN

Figure 83. That far flung ring of revolving clouds tries to hide its evolution behind a veil of atoms, which will neither shine by their own light nor allow other light to pass through. Perhaps they are atoms and electrons which have "done their bit," and have retired to the outskirts for an almost eternal rest. The fourth in Sir James Jeans series. (From a photograph of N.G.C. 4594, constellation of Virgo, taken at the Mt. Wilson Observatory, May 3, 1916, with the telescope 5 feet in diameter. Exposure 2¼ hours. Courtesy of the Mt. Wilson Observatory.)

THE GLOWING BALL HAS BECOME A SPIRAL NEBULA

Figure 84. With a small primeval and brilliant center, this disc of clouds of gas and dark obscuring matter commences to condense into sparkling stars. The fifth and last in this special series where the shapes computed by Sir James Jeans correspond with those of these photographs. (From a photograph of N.G.C. 4565, Coma Berenices, taken at the Mt. Wilson Observatory, March 6 and 7, 1910, with the telescope 5 feet in diameter. Exposure 5 hours. Courtesy of the Mt. Wilson Observatory.)

THIS NEBULA HAS NEVER BEEN MUCH DISTORTED BY AN ENCOUNTER

Figure 85. Even this beautiful annular nebula shows a slight trace of spiral form. (N.G.C. 7217 Pegasus. From a photograph taken September 2, 1913, at the Mt. Wilson Observatory with the telescope 5 feet in diameter. Exposure 5½ hours. Courtesy of the Mt. Wilson Observatory.)

THE GREAT NEBULA OF ANDROMEDA

Figure 86. At a distance of nearly 900,000 light years, and with a width of 45,000 light years, this spiral nebula boasts of several thousands million suns. Like flakes of snow, the stars between us and this nebula cover the whole picture. It is visible to the naked eye as a blurred star. (N.G.C. 224. From a photograph taken at the Yerkes Observatory of the University of Chicago. Courtesy of the Yerkes Observatory.)

and star clusters. In the following chapters we will learn more about this change from gas to star. At present we can realize that this is going on, for we can actually see the stars in some of the photographs which were brought back by the meteor.

Even after a nebula has changed into thousands of millions of stars, we can consider it as delicate, for it is held together only by the mutual gravitation of its members, like our Milky Way. Of course, any other very massive body which came into the neighborhood might seriously disturb the arrangement of such a nebula.

These nebulae are prodigious. The Great Nebula of Androm-eda (Figure 86) is 45,000 light-years in diameter and a million light-years from the earth. Yet it is visible to the naked eye as a faint, blurred point. We can hardly imagine so enormous an object without at the same time thinking it massive. It may be much denser at the center, but for the most part the nebula, before it becomes very flattened, was like the thinnest gas you can imagine. In fact, it is reported on good authority that when that meteor started to photograph his first nebula, he actually got thousands of miles inside and never even realized it.

It was about 10,000 million years ago that the sun had that narrow escape from collision with a star described in Chapter IV. At that time those gigantic masses of the sun's liquid and gaseous substance were thrown out. They were thrown into space in two great arms, which first uncoiled from the sun in

145

spirals like a watch spring. In throwing part of itself away in this peculiar manner, because of the terrific pull of the passing star, the sun obeyed certain laws of mathematics. Undoubtedly he did, for F. R. Moulton of Chicago University has computed that he did just this thing and could have done nothing else— so severe are the laws of mathematics.

Perhaps these island universes in the course of millions of millions of years come fairly near each other. If they do, then they, too, must have to obey the laws of mathematics and send part of themselves out into space in two spiral arms. But since these nebulae are delicate ethereal creatures, mere clusters of stars, they are seriously disturbed if another nebula passes even at a great distance. They then act just the same as the sun did. They throw out two spiral arms. More exactly, that great flat disc at the equator breaks up into two spiral arms which wrap themselves around the glowing center. The kindly meteor took the trouble to drive his sunbeam as far as the constellation where live the dogs of Venaticus. In Latin it is called Canis Venatici. There he photographed for us the famous "whirlpool" nebula (Figure 87) which, according to Sir James Jeans of Cambridge, may have been badly distorted by some passing rival. So many island universes have been distorted in this way that we generally speak of them as "spiral nebulae."

Figure 88 is a photograph of what may be two nebulae passing each other in space. The upper nebula clearly shows the two

THE GREAT WHIRLPOOL NEBULA OF CANIS VENATICI

Figure 87. This great island universe either has turned or is turning into stars. Some near-collision has distorted it to the spiral shape. Because it looks like one of our whirlpools it has been given that name. Unlike a whirlpool, the stars are not moving toward the center. There are indications that they are traveling out from the center as the nebula as a whole revolves around its nucleus. Although each little point of light in this nebula is moving several scores of miles per second, its distance is so great that two photographs taken ten years apart, and examined with microscopes show hardly any change. (The Nebulae N.G.C. 5194-5. From a photograph taken May 15, 1926, at the Mt. Wilson Observatory with the telescope 8 feet in diameter. Exposure 3 hours. Courtesy of Mt. Wilson Observatory.)

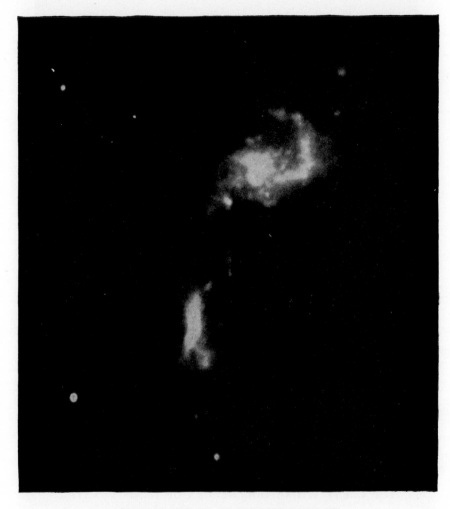

TWO NEBULAE PASS IN THE NIGHT

Figure 88. Perhaps these two nebulae are distorting one another as they pass by. Great tidal forces may cause the flattened disc to become spiral arms. (N.G.C. 3395 and 3396. "Suggestive of tidal action," according to Sir James Jeans in *The Universe Around Us*, published by the Macmillan Co. From a photograph taken at Mt. Wilson Observatory. Courtesy of Mt. Wilson Observatory.)

great arms which are being formed, perhaps by the attraction of the lower nebula. It is difficult to see what is happening to the lower nebula. Some day a giant telescope may tell us more about this mysterious pair.

XXIV: THE BIRTH OF STARS

ow we come to a new and very important period in the life of a spiral nebula: those unwinding arms, far-flung from the glowing center, shrink, become narrow, and break up into small clouds. In the nebula in the Great Bear, Figure 89, you can see that the change is taking place. The arms are beginning to look like a string of small earth clouds.

That traveling meteor would probably laugh at us if he heard us call them "small." He would recall how he spent a thousand earth years passing just one of the so-called "small clouds." We must remember that from the end of one arm to the end of another it is possibly 40,000 light-years.

The changes in the spiral nebulae do not stop with the formation of two long strings of cosmic pearls. Each "pearl" or glowing cloud continues to shrink and to break up into thousands and millions of sparkling objects. These objects become stars, suns like our sun.

A good example of this stage in the life history of a spiral is

148

LIKE MILLIONS OF CRYSTALS THESE ARMS ARE TURNING INTO STARS

Figure 89. A beautiful spiral nebula in the constellation Ursa Major, the Great Bear. This is one of the pictures selected by Sir James Jeans to illustrate the evolution of a star cloud from a nebula, in his book *The Universe Around Us,* published by the Macmillan Company. (From a photograph of N.G.C. 3031 taken at the Mt. Wilson Observatory, February 5, 1919, with the telescope 5 feet in diameter; exposure 4 hours and 15 minutes. Courtesy of Mt. Wilson Observatory.)

THE NEBULA IS GROWING OLD

Figure 90. Millions of suns in compact clusters are all that remain of the graceful spiral arms of which the nebula was once so proud. This nebula also was selected by Sir James Jeans to represent a typical stage in evolution. (From a photograph of N.G.C. 5457, Ursa Major, taken at the Mt. Wilson Observatory March 10 and 11, 1910, with the 60-inch telescope; exposure 7 hours and 30 minutes. Courtesy of the Mt. Wilson Observatory.)

the nebula in Figure 90. Here the center apparently still is a glowing mass of electrons and atoms. The arms have unwound to a considerable extent—the clock is running down. The little clouds in each arm have shrunk and condensed into brilliant star clusters. There are thousands of these spots and each spot must contain thousands of brilliant stars which we might say have just been born.

After another 1,000 million years or so, the original location of these arms becomes more or less lost. Star clusters and individual stars now predominate. To show us an island universe which had reached this age, the kindly meteor drove his sunbeam into the constellation of the Triangle (Triangulum) and photographed all that was left of an old spiral (Figure 91). Nearly all of this old spiral has turned into stars. Where the stars are most numerous, you can still trace the shape of those two original arms. Now they have become so extended as almost to form a straight line. There probably are thousands of millions of stars in this island universe.

To photograph a final stage—no, "final" is not the right word: we know no more about the end than we do about the beginning; so let us call it simply the next stage. To show us then what the nebula in Figure 91 will look like at some time in the future, the meteor ran down to the southern hemisphere and photographed a great star cluster called the Greater of the Clouds of Magellan (Figure 92). Here all trace of the old spiral seems to have disappeared. We have, merely, countless millions of stars and star clusters.

Our meteor then said that his sunbeam was tired and he refused to go again on a journey of thousands of years; for he had been asked to travel for 10 million years up beyond the North Star and then to photograph our own galaxy—our group of island universes. Since we cannot get this valuable photograph we must do the best we can to imagine what our Milky Way would look like if seen from far off in space.

Before we have finished this exploration of interstellar space, we may find that our sun is in the midst of a cluster of island universes. Some of these spiral nebulae may actually be in collision. Some may be partly hidden by great dust clouds. Several may be so grouped as to give us that band of light we call the Milky Way. Finally, we may find that our sun is merely an insignificant member of one of these spiral nebulae.

By the help of the kindly meteor and the wise old comet, we have seen almost a museum of nebulae. We have watched the round glowing ball of atoms and electrons shrink and revolve. We have seen the edge thrown out at the equator. Then came the disturbance caused by a passing nebula and the production of the two spiral arms. As the nebula grew older these arms unwound and condensed into clouds of enormous size. Finally the clouds became star clusters, and the star clusters merged into one huge mass of individual stars. Occasionally

A STAR CLOUD WHICH STILL SHOWS ITS NEBULAR ANCESTRY

Figure 91. The old spiral form can be traced among the thousands of compact star clusters, according to Sir James Jeans of Cambridge University, England. E. P. Hubble of the Mt. Wilson Observatory finds that it takes light 15,000 years to cross from one side of this star cloud to another. (From a photograph of N.G.C. 598, Triangulum, taken at the Mt. Wilson Observatory July 26, 1925, with the Hooker telescope 8 feet in diameter; exposure 1 hour and 30 minutes. Courtesy of Mt. Wilson Observatory.)

THE LARGER OF THE TWO CLOUDS OF MAGELLAN

Figure 92. To the naked eye this cloud of stars looks like a section of the Milky Way which has wandered away to within about twenty degrees of the South Celestial Pole. Here several hundred thousand stars are assembled in some unknown formation. The light by which this photograph was taken left the cloud over 100,000 years ago. This great distance is growing greater at the rate of five thousand million miles per year.

The stars in this picture look faint merely because of the enormous distance. If we should explore the cloud we would find that many of the stars are much brighter than the sun. One of these stars changes in brightness from time to time for some unknown reason. It is called S. Doradus, and occasionally it becomes five hundred thousand times brighter than our sun; yet due to its distance from us it always is from our point of view a telescopic star. (From a photograph taken in the Southern Hemisphere by Prof. Schaeberle of the Lick Observatory. Courtesy of the Lick Observatory.)

one star came near enough to another to cause masses of gas and liquid to be thrown into space. From this débris planets were formed. Ultimately, life appeared on probably a few of these planets.

More could be said in regard to a still earlier stage, and also in regard to a later stage. However, let us close this chapter with that stage in the sun's history in which life could appear on a planet.

XXV: SUPER-GALAXY

HESE island universes, a million light-years apart, seem to be so gigantic that it is hard to imagine that they move. Yet their velocities are great. Therefore, it would seem as if sometimes many of the nebulae might come much closer together, and perhaps even collide. We already have found that two or more of these nebulae occasionally come so close together as to distort each other and turn a nice, smooth, flattened nebula into a spiral nebula.

Now we know that there are certain regions in space where nebulae foregather. Like birds, they flock together. Figures 93 and 94 are photographs of such a thickly settled community of nebulae. This is a part of a very democratic nebula country, for there are plain nebulae, curiously shaped nebulae and island universes. All kinds are gathering here. Shall we say that they are coming from the far depths of space? We do not know. We merely see these nebulae, each of a size so large that it is beyond our comprehension, gathering together like a flock of ducks. One great collection of nebulae is in the direction of the

A POPULAR PLACE FOR NEBULAE

Figure 93. For untold ages these nebulae have been traveling toward this meeting place. Those stars you see in the photograph are all nearby. You are looking through a thin curtain of stars in our own spiral nebula. Far out where these nebulae are meeting there is only dark and interminable space. Of course the nebulae light their own way much as automobiles do. Some are round glowing clouds from which thousands of millions of stars will be formed. Others, with graceful spiral arms, already have become brilliant star clusters, which at this enormous distance look like wisps of smoke. Apparently these nebulae are in approximately the same plane, so that if a tiny planet revolved around a tiny star in a spiral arm near the center of this group, the thinking animals on such a planet would see a brilliant band of stars in their sky. Some day they might realize, as we do, that such a band was really caused by a number of spiral nebulae seen on edge. According to Harlow Shapley of the Astronomical Observatory of Harvard College, this is a good example of a super-galaxy not unlike the one which causes our Milky Way. (From a photograph of N.G.C. 7317-20, Pegasus, taken at Mt. Wilson Observatory August 26 and 27, 1916, with the telescope 5 feet in diameter; exposure 45 minutes. Courtesy of Mt. Wilson Observatory.)

THE CLANS ARE GATHERING

Figure 94. In the lower right hand corner there is one small nebula which is turning its edge toward us. It seems to be about the same age as the nebula in Figure 82, "An Equatorial Bulge Becomes a Ring." On the extreme right there is apparently a primitive nebula, like Figure 80, "A Glowing Ball of Enormous Size." Below, and to the left of this primitive nebula, there is one which has just produced two very faint arms. Finally, in the extreme upper left hand corner and below just to the left of the center, there are two well-developed spirals which to some extent resemble the Great Nebula of Andromeda, Figure 86. Are these nebulae gathering together to make a super-galaxy? Three of those spirals seem to be facing in the same direction. Some day they may make a brilliant milky way for a thinking animal on a planet revolving around one of their stars. (From a photograph of N.G.C. 7782 taken at the Mt. Wilson Observatory, September 17, 1917, with the telescope 60 inches in diameter. Courtesy of the Mt. Wilson Observatory.)

SPIRAL NEBULA ON EDGE

Figure 95. Apparently a thin sheet of cosmic dust almost divides this nebula by obscuring the light. If we were on a planet revolving around a star in one of the spiral arms of this nebula, we probably would see this thin layer of dust as a brightly illuminated cloud. (From a photograph of N.G.C. 891, Andromeda, taken at the Mt. Wilson Observatory November 23 and 24, 1916, with the telescope 5 feet in diameter, exposure 7 hours and 15 minutes. Courtesy of Mt. Wilson Observatory.)

STAR CLOUDS IN SAGITTARIUS

Figure 96. A spiral nebula nearby and seen from the edge. That tame meteor must have had many such views as he approached some of those island universes. This spiral is of course part of our own super-galaxy—our own Milky Way. Those dark patches of celestial dust we have often seen before near the spiral arms of island universes. (From a photograph taken at the Mt. Wilson Observatory with the Tessar lens on July 21, 1922; exposure 3-3/4 hours. Courtesy of the Mt. Wilson Observatory.)

constellations of Coma and Virgo. Nearly 3,000 have been counted in this vast gathering and many more may yet be found.

So through the interminable stretches of space we have not merely island universes, but large clusters of nebulae and spirals. Except here and there they are not elbowing each other for lack of room. Most of them are probably a million light-years from their nearest neighbor. It is estimated that 30 million nebulae are within the range of the telescope, eight feet in diameter, at the Mt. Wilson Observatory in California. In some cases, each neighbor consists of several thousand million stars. About some star in such a spiral nebula a planet may be revolving, and on that tiny speck some thinking creatures may have been developed. Perhaps they have become adept in astronomy. They may have built telescopes and explored the space around them.

First these thinking animals would discover that the great white band in their sky was in reality a mass of stars. Then they would learn that their sun was only one of several thousand million suns which made up their cluster—their spiral nebula.

As they increased the size of their telescopes they would find other island universes millions of light-years away. Then they would discover that these nebulae were not uniformly distributed in space. Perhaps they would look up to our Milky Way

Galaxy and say: "Many nebulae are hovering around that spiral. There are huge star clouds in its neighborhood, and near by there are some wonderful spiral nebulae. How brilliant the sky must be in that great flattened cluster of spiral nebulae and star clusters!"

Possibly the creature on such a far-off member of the Coma-Virgo group of nebulae is telling the truth, if he is telling anything. This is the very frontier of our exploration. We know that these great island universes, and equally great globular nebulae, gather together in immense clouds. This is obvious because we can see them. We know that our galaxy is a member of such a group; but we do not know the exact character of our cloud of galaxies and cannot know it for some time to come.

You remember that the earth grew through thousands of millions of years by attracting to itself innumerable meteors —the débris of that accident which befell our sun. The moon, perhaps, also grew in the same way. Now the earth by its greater attraction holds the moon in captivity. Perhaps our flock of spirals and star clusters has grown by attracting, through a vastly greater length of time, many nebulae and spirals.

Some of these groups of nebulae, like the super-galaxy in Centaurus, have become flattened and are shaped something

IS THIS SOME ANIMAL'S MILKY WAY?

Figure 97. This island universe in the constellation of Cepheus may represent in appearance one of the spiral nebulae which make our super-galaxy. The star clouds, which make the Milky Way in the constellations of Sagittarius and Ophiuchus, may be such a spiral nebula seen on edge. (From a photograph of N.G.C. 6946, taken June 19 and 20, 1922, with the telescope 8 feet in diameter; exposure 4 hours. Courtesy of the Mt. Wilson Observatory.)

STAR CLOUD IN THE CONSTELLATION OF SCUTUM SOBIESKI

Figure 98. According to Harlow Shapley of the Harvard College Observatory, this star cloud may be a spiral nebula seen on edge, but so near that we cannot see it as a long narrow spindle of light. If it weren't for the dark nebulae which are clearly shown in the picture, it would be a very brilliant part of the sky. (From a photograph taken at the Yerkes Observatory, and reproduced by permission of the University of Chicago Press. Courtesy of the Yerkes Observatory.)

like a watch. You would naturally suppose that this is due to rapid spinning, whereby the poles became flattened and the equator bulged until at last the whole group looked as thin and flat as a watch. The nebulae in such super-galaxies are so faint and so far off that such a whirlpool motion, if it exists, cannot be measured by the small telescopes at our disposal.

Even to an astronomer the length of time required to develop such a formation seems prodigious. Apparently from various sources these nebulae were drawn together. Probably the individuals came to the gathering place from distances that must have been measured by tens of millions of light-years.

That first mustering of these raw nebula recruits would take an almost inconceivably long time. When they finally did come together, they would be a confused crowd, more like a lot of sparrows than like an orderly flock of geese. Then began the contest for leadership. Finally some nebulae larger and swifter than others predominated. They forced the others by their attraction to swing around the circle their way. This frontier settlement, where every nebula wanted to go his own way, at last became an orderly whirlpool of nebulae, all revolving in the same direction and in nearly the same plane.

Our sun is a tiny speck in such a flattened super-galaxy. It is a member of a spiral nebula which has become so disintegrated that it is almost a star cloud. From far out in space such a cloud may look something like the nebula called N.Y.C. 891 (Figure 95). Our Milky Way is in part caused by this thin layer of stars.

There are many other spiral nebulae in our super-galaxy— our whirlpool—which help to brighten the Milky Way. The stars in our own spiral nebula are near by, while those belonging to other spirals are farther away. If you look toward the constellations of Ophiuchus and Sagittarius, you will see a section of the Milky Way which is for the most part very distant. Those bright clouds of stars (Figure 96) are part of a spiral nebula which in size and shape may be much like the nebula in Cepheus (Figure 97). As we see those masses of cloud we are looking "edge on" at the nebula. Hence the brilliancy of that row of star clouds. This spiral probably is more than 100,000 light-years from us. That brilliant patch of Milky Way light in the constellation of Scutum Sobieski (Figure 98) probably is another spiral nebula which we see only from its edge, for it lies in the plane of our super-galaxy. So our celestial whirlpool, by means of perhaps dozens and scores of spiral nebulae and star clouds, helps to make our Milky Way brilliant on any dark night.

There are some star clusters in our super-galaxy which are very compact and much smaller than these great spirals we have been describing. They are so round that they are called globular star clusters. However, each one contains thousands

OMEGA CENTAURI

Figure 99. A famous globular cluster in the constellation of the Centaur; visible only in the Southern hemisphere. To the naked eye this is a faint blurred star, not quite so bright as most of the stars in the Big Dipper. There are perhaps a hundred thousand stars in this cluster. It is so far off that the light which it gives today left the cluster 21,000 years ago. At that time on the earth, the human race was just recovering from the trying times of the Great Ice Age. (From a photograph taken at the Harvard College Branch Observatory at Arequipa, Peru, June 7, 1897, with the Boyden telescope, 13 inches in diameter; exposure 40 minutes. Courtesy of the Harvard College Observatory.)

A VERY DISTANT STAR CLOUD

Figure 100. Invisible to the naked eye, this distant star cloud was photographed with a telescope 8 feet in diameter. According to research by E. P. Hubble, the light by which we see these stars today has been traveling toward us for 700,000 years. It started on this long journey when the Heidelberg man was living in Germany. The first great glacier of the Pleistocene Period had come and gone, and Europe and America were enjoying a milder climate than usual. (From a photograph of N.G.C. 6822 taken at the Mt. Wilson Observatory July 10, 1923, with the Hooker telescope 8 feet in diameter; exposure 3½ hours. Courtesy of Mt. Wilson Observatory.)

of stars and perhaps hundred of thousands (Figure 17 and 99). A few of these clusters are found far out in space. Figure 100 is a photograph of a cluster which is 700,000 light-years away. Notwithstanding such a distance, it may be classed by that thinking animal in the Coma-Virgo group as part of our super-galaxy; part of our great group of nebulae and star clusters.

We judge from such photographs as Figures 88, 93, and 101, that these spiral nebulae and globular star clusters some-times come into collision with each other. It is interesting to speculate on what would happen to us if our spiral nebula collided with another in our super-galaxy. We don't have to draw much on our imagination, for Harlow Shapley thinks there is evidence that such an interesting event now is taking place. There is some reason to believe that our spiral now is in collision with the spiral which appears to us as a bright cloud of stars in the Milky Way in the constellation of Cygnus (Figure 102).

Apparently we are in no danger, for the spaces between the stars are enormous even in a crowded nebula. Hundreds of millions of years from now, that part of the Milky Way may be more brilliant as these two spirals continue to crash into each other.

When two spiral nebulae collide, their spiral formation probably is destroyed. They unite to form, after hundreds of

157

millions of years, a more or less shapeless cloud of stars. It may be on such occasions that a few of the stars come close enough together to form planets.

About a million light-years away we see the Andromeda nebula (Figure 86). Here, also, we have a vast spiral of several thousand million stars. On the edge of this magnificent object we see two other nebulae. Are they ultimately to be absorbed by this island universe? It looks as if they were about to sink their individuality in that brilliant collection of stars which we call the Great Nebula of Andromeda.

Perhaps the Andromeda nebula revolves around the center of our flattened cluster of spirals in much the way that some comets, together with all the planets, are revolving around the center of the solar system. Many, many others of the cloud of nebulae in our neighborhood may do likewise. Long ages from now some others may join us and make our group bigger; apparently others in the past already have done so.

Near us, about 100,000 light-years away, there are the clouds of Magellan, which we already have mentioned (Figures 26 and 92). They consist of millions of stars. Possibly they were parts of a great nebula which flattened and became spiral in shape. Then not only the arms but the very center condensed into stars. Perhaps, due to some celestial catastrophe, it broke and these clouds are part of the débris. They foregathered with us in our part of space. There are other star clouds like them,

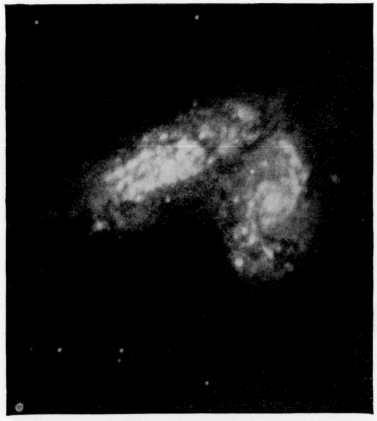

ARE THESE TWO ISLAND UNIVERSES COLLIDING?

Figure 101. Perhaps these two spiral nebulae are "sideswiping" each other. They probably are moving at tremendous speed. Their enormous distance from us makes their motion difficult to measure during the short time that we have had large telescopes. Each spiral consists of thousands of millions of stars. An animal on a planet revolving around one of those stars would see most of the other stars in his spiral as a distant band of light, which he might call his "milky way." If he looked toward the other spiral he would see the distant band of light was more intense in that direction. His astronomers might tell him that there is another spiral which is colliding with his spiral, and therefore making his "milky way" in one part of his sky so very brilliant. (From a photograph of N.G.C. 4567-8, constellation of Virgo, taken at the Mt. Wilson Observatory March 22, May 19, 1914, with the telescope 5 feet in diameter; exposure 6 hours. This photograph is identical with Figure 18. Courtesy of the Mt. Wilson Observatory.)

CONSTELLATIONS OF DELPHINUS AND CYGNUS

Figure 102. After drawings in *Atlas Coelestis* by Eduard Heis, professor of mathematics at the Royal Academy at Munster.

but much fainter and more distant. A photograph of such a one is reproduced in Figure 100.

Apparently all spirals have "dust clouds" hovering around on the flattened edge, and perhaps between the spiral arms. The spirals in our super-galaxy seem to be no exception, for these local dust clouds obscure the sky in places and cause those "dark nebulae." In the neighborhood of the constellation of Cygnus (Figure 102), an obscuring cloud of this character divides the Milky Way into two parts. Of course, the Milky Way is not really cut in this way; it merely appears to be, because this mass of dust, probably from the unfolding arms of our own local spiral, cuts off our view. It is too bad that it does; for it is there that the collision between our spiral and the "Cygnus Spiral" is occurring. It looks as if celestial destroyers were laying a smoke screen to hide some maneuver in the great battle which is raging between these spirals.

XXVI: LIGHT AND GRAVITY FIGHTING FOR THE NEBULA

EVER since Galileo first poked a hole through that imaginary medieval rampart with his one-inch telescope, we have been exploring farther back in time. We have been trying our best to discover the origin of all things. Sometimes we have not been very successful; but, after decades, we usually have discovered our errors and once again we have returned to the true trail.

On the earth, so far as geography is concerned, our search for unknown lands must some day cease; for at some time in the future all land will be explored and mapped, and doubtless even photographed from the air. In the great space around us and in us, the exploration can probably go on forever; for it is unlikely that we will ever discover the real origin or even the real nature of electrons, protons, time, velocity, and life.

We are something like the ancient Egyptians. They were very highly civilized and discovered a great deal about the world around them; but although they lived on the banks of the Nile River, they never knew where it came from. So far as the Egyptians knew, the waters of the Nile came from the mysterious forests of Africa, and ultimately flowed into the Mediterranean Sea. The Mediterranean joined with the Atlantic Ocean, which to the Egyptians was a vast stretch of uncharted sea. Yet the Egyptians about 2,000 years ago, because of the work of the Greeks, knew that the earth was round. They knew, then, something about the extent of their earthly world and its shape, and even how many miles it was in diameter.

Notwithstanding all this knowledge, they did not know the sources of the river on which they lived, and did not know how far the Atlantic Ocean extended toward the west. It wasn't until approximately 1,500 years later that Columbus discovered the other side of the Atlantic Ocean, and it was less than 100 years ago that it was found that the Nile flows from a great lake in the heart of Africa. So we cannot blame the Egyptians for being so ignorant about geography.

We pursue the origin of electrons and protons, in iron, in the air, and in elbows. Then we hunt for the origin of stars and island universes and clouds of nebulae. Yet we never find whence they came and we know not to what end they are going. However, the mere exploring is a fascinating sport, so let us see how far back we can reasonably go toward the origin of the nebula.

Let us assume, as Sir James Jeans has done, that once upon

a time vast stretches of space were filled with electrons and protons, perhaps many of them in the form of atoms. When we say "filled" we don't mean so close together as molecules of water in a pail. Each atom or each electron was perhaps miles from its nearest neighbor. If we had such a bit of space in our laboratory, we would call it a perfect vacuum. Yet the weight of all these atoms and electrons was equal to that of thousands of island universes—so great was the extent of this part of primeval space. These atoms were not stationary. They moved here and there among themselves, and sometimes in widely scattered groups.

Naturally they came together after an exceedingly long time, because they attracted each other, in just the way that the earth attracted those meteors thousands of millions of years ago. These atoms, however, as they came together had to play the game according to certain rules.

First you remember that atoms are very nervous. At the slightest provocation they dart around at high speed. In this case the provocation was that they were getting closer together and hitting each other. This caused heat, and when the motion became very great, it caused light.

A second rule of the game was connected with our old friend the "velocity of escape." You remember that the moon has no air because it isn't powerful enough to keep the atoms of air from bouncing away. The moon is so light that it cannot attract the atoms of air with sufficient force to keep them from running away into space. The earth, on the other hand, is so large that by its attraction it holds the atoms of the air right on its surface, which is very fortunate for us and all the other animals.

A vast group of far-flung atoms would behave like the earth. The combined attraction of them all would keep the nervous members from bouncing away. On the other hand, if a small group of atoms got together and said: "We are going to form a nebula which will some day condense and become a spiral," they would not succeed. Their combined attraction would be so little that the individual atoms would run away and soon there would be none left to carry out the ambitious plan.

Evidently, if a dust cloud of atoms is smaller than a certain size, it will just expand and expand, and the nervous atoms will eventually disappear; but if it is bigger than a certain size, it will hold its excitable atoms, which will move toward each other so that the cloud will grow denser and smaller.

If these flights of our imagination are true, we would not expect to find any very small island universes, or even any very small stars. We might, however, think that we could find examples of stars and nebulae of almost inconceivable size and weight. That is not so. Island universes are noted more for their similarity in size than for their differences. While some are larger and some are smaller, yet they do not vary enormously in size or in weight. This sameness in size also applies to the stars. There is no star known which is as much as 100 times heavier than our sun, nor any star so far discovered which is 100 times lighter.

Such approximate regularity cannot be due to chance. There must be some reason for it and that reason is extremely interesting. It is closely connected with comets' tails. You will remember that a comet's tail always points away from the sun. This is because light has driving power like wind. To be sure, it is an extremely tiny force; but then an atom also is an extremely tiny speck.

Now think what will happen when our enormous dust cloud begins to contract. The individual atoms, attracted by all the others, begin to fall toward the center. The dust cloud becomes denser; the atoms hit each other more frequently; first heat and then light is developed, and this is the first rule of the game which our ancestral nebula has to obey. Some of the atoms commence to explode and the beginning of a glowing nebula is made. Quanta or protons are let loose and they try to get out from the uncomfortably crowded interior of the dust cloud which we now can call a nebula. They keep colliding with atoms and electrons which are falling toward the center.

At first the confusion is bad, but neither of these contending forces can seriously disturb the other. The atoms keep on falling toward the center, although the quanta are constantly pushing into them and trying to force them back to outer space. The atoms handle the quanta roughly and shove them to one side. Yet the quanta, bouncing from one atom to another, with sometimes long straight dashes, always struggle toward outer space. As these quanta—these bullets of energy, these rays of light—reach the outer layers of this great dust cloud, they find that the atoms are moving less furiously. Occasionally a quantum is able to stop an atom right in his tracks. This is because the atom is so far from the center of the nebula that he is being attracted only feebly. Stretching all around the nebula's center like a great hollow shell, these contending forces fight a drawn battle; victory will come to neither side.

Unlike Xenophon's Greek phalanx, the atoms are not arrayed in serried ranks. They are approaching the center of the nebula against the opposition of the quanta more like a skirmish line. From an atom's point of view there is a long distance between himself and his nearest neighbors. Perhaps it is better to call this shell of atoms, moving toward the center, a number of scouts rather than a skirmish line. Therefore, many, many quanta break through and continue their journey to outer space. They are quicker than cavalry or airplanes, for they go with the speed of light.

All the quanta cannot gain their freedom so easily. Beyond this line of battle where the forces are equal, there is a vast extent of dust cloud. These outer layers, being very far from the attracting center, are moving feebly and slowly. Now it is the quanta's turn to be victorious. They not only stop the slowly moving atoms, but actually drive them back to outer space.

At this point let us declare an armistice and look about us. Of that great chunk of the primeval dust cloud only those atoms remain which were inside that zone where the fight was so fierce that neither side could win. All those great reserve forces of atoms which were coming slowly to the assistance of their hard-pressed friends, have been driven by the darting quanta to the eternal darkness of primeval space.

Like a safety valve, the repulsive power of light will not allow a star or nebula to become too large. Only a limited number of atoms can come together to form an organized nebula, then a spiral nebula, and finally a galaxy.

In both directions the nebulae are limited. If too few atoms try to come together, they will not succeed. The power of attraction will be less than the nervous force of the atoms as they bounce and run away. In other words, the atom's velocity is greater than the group's velocity of escape. If the cloud of atoms is too large, the increasing intensity of the light from the center drives the outer layers away.

Some may say this is pure imagination, and, to a certain extent, it is. Perhaps it would be better to say that this is orderly and systematized imagination, which is a very different thing from the daydream of an ancient philosopher. To an imaginary dust cloud Sir James Jeans has applied well-known laws: the laws of gravity, light, and heat. He has shown us how the objects we see around us have been derived from that primeval cloud. At present we cannot go beyond this imaginary dust cloud.

Perhaps there never was just one dust cloud breaking up into units, and thus causing millions of island universes. It may be such clouds are perpetually forming, breaking into sections and condensing. But to speculate further would be unrestrained imagination and beyond the control of our knowledge of light, gravity, time, and space.

XXVII:
PROVING THE INCREDIBLE

E HAVE wandered far and wide in this mysterious universe. Everywhere we found space, empty space, the most common thing in all the universe. The Milky Way—that white river on which spirit Pharaohs sailed—proved upon investigation to be mostly empty space with here and there a star. Mr. Eddington's table, and even his own elbow, were found to be will-o'-the-wisps—mere ghosts of objects.

Then, at last, we examined the atom. To our amazement we found that it is not the very hard and almost inconceivably small ball that our ancestors imagined. It is, instead, a little group of electrons and protons. To a bug on an electron in Mr. Eddington's table, other electron and proton systems would seem as distant, and the world as full of empty space, as it does to us on this earth when we look up to the sky on a clear and dark night. Let us try to imagine what the world would be like as seen from the surface of an electron.

A tiny phantom engineer-bug might bore a hole through a real electron. When he had crawled through, and sat upon the other side to view his achievement with satisfaction, he might say to his associates: "I am glad I don't have to bore this hole all the way to that proton about which this electron is revolving; for the astronomer-bug has told me that the proton is 50 thousand times as far off as the length of this tunnel. Yet how clearly we can see it—it doesn't look so far away!

"That same wise bug told me there are other electrons revolving around other protons, and that the world is full of such systems. Sometimes I have seen one of those systems appear from the great blank distance, dash before me, and disappear again. It seems as if they were going to strike us but they never do.

"The blue bug who studies physics told me that our little proton and electron system was sending out a mysterious force which prevents these roving systems from hitting us. The little red history-bug told me that thousands of electron-years ago the sky was full of these wandering systems. The little red bug's ancestors got very nervous because they were afraid that one of these systems would hit the proton and destroy all life upon their electron. The big green astronomer-bug said that bad accidents do happen, and that sometimes a mysterious object called a quantum sweeps down like a vast cloud and envelops both the proton and electron. Then all life perishes. Out of the turmoil a new system appears with the electrons revolving farther from the proton."

169

PROVING THE INCREDIBLE

The friends of the engineer-bug looked at him with amazement. Yet they knew the engineer-bug had done some wonderful things. He had taught them how to make electricity with which they had bored this great tunnel straight through the electron. Other wise bugs had made telescopes by which they could see distant systems which were dashing around in space. The history-bug had dug up many ancient records. Therefore, the friends of the engineer-bug were ready to learn some of the true things about the world, because these wise bugs had proved their wisdom by so many discoveries. They no longer believed some of the funny stories about men who shot apples off the heads of their children, and young boys who cut down cherry trees with hatchets, and queer people who lived on the top of Mt. Olympus and behaved like ordinary electron-bugs but yet could be invisible when they wished.

Of course an electron-year is the time it takes an electron to go once around the proton. These wise phantom bugs had found that it was 1,000 million electron-years since life first had appeared upon this electron. They had discovered that at first life was represented by inconceivably minute specks which were invisible even in their most powerful microscopes. Then, in millions of electron-years, life had developed until now there were red history-bugs, green astronomy-bugs, engineer-bugs, and blue bugs who study physics.

It has been only recently that the ape-men who live upon

one of the planets, have been able to compare a planet-year with an electron-year. During the last thirty years they have found that it takes at least 1,000 million electron-years to make one second of earth time.

Scientists, of course, have never really found phantom colored electron-bugs, yet they know something about the length of an electron-year. We have thus begun to realize that space is as mysterious and unfathomable inside Mr. Eddington's elbow, as it is in the sky and among the stars.

If we traveled through space forever, would we always be passing one great star cluster after another? Is there no limit to the number of island universes in the world? Is an electron mostly empty space, and does it also consist of a multitude of tiny systems? What is this queer thing we call time? Would it be the same on the surface of an electron as it is for us?

During the last century a well-educated scientist would have answered: "I do not know," to all of these questions. However, 3,000 years ago the leading men and women would probably have given an answer to each question. It would have been a foolish set of answers and the result of pure imagination. It is a curious characteristic of ignorant and semi-barbarous people that they always can explain everything, and it is only the most intelligent people who have the courage to say that they don't know the answer to many questions.

During the present century some of these age-old questions

have been at least partially answered. Such men as H. A. Lorentz, George F. FitzGerald, and Albert Einstein have given us an outline of many important areas in our map of knowledge. Perhaps we cannot understand all of their arguments and mathematical analyses. Even some of the results are beyond our comprehension. Yet we can all see the universe a little more correctly as a result of the researches of these men. Let us see how far we can go in understanding these modern discoveries.

If you drive with the wind in an automobile, you will not feel the air so much, even in a perfectly open car, as you would if you turned around and drove directly against the wind. So Michelson (Figure 104) and Morley argued that when the earth is going 18 miles a second directly toward the source of light, the waves of light ought to rush past much faster than when the earth was going at the same terrific speed in the opposite direction, that is, with the stream of light. To verify this simple idea they measured the velocity of light carefully under all conditions. They were amazed to find that the velocity of light was the same as observed from the earth, whether they were going 18 miles per second with it or against it. Imagine your surprise if you found that the wind was always blowing past your car with the same speed, no matter whether you were driving against the wind or driving with the wind. You would say such an experience could only be true in

ALBERT EINSTEIN

Figure 103. The greatest scientist of the present epoch. Born in Ulm, Würt-
temberg, Germany, he was educated in the Polytechnic School at Zurich while
supporting himself by teaching mathematics and physics. Later he was made
director of the Kaiser Wilhelm Physical Institute at Berlin. Albert Einstein has
made remarkable progress in proving the relationship between the various things
which make up our world, such as: velocity, time, mass, and light. In this way
he demonstrates the essential unity of all the features of the universe. The phenomenon of life is the only subject which has been omitted. (Reproduced by
permission of the University of Chicago Press. Courtesy of the Yerkes Observatory.)

ALBERT ABRAHAM MICHELSON

Figure 104. A. A. Michelson, one of America's most famous physicists, was born in 1852 at Strelno in Germany, and was taken by his parents to California when a child. In 1873, he was graduated from the United States Naval Academy where he taught physics for several years. He died in May, 1931.

Michelson measured the velocity of light with greater accuracy than had been previously attained. He invented the interferometer, and by means of it the diameter of the red star Beta Orionis was measured by F. G. Pease at the Mt. Wilson Observatory. This star proved to be larger than even the orbit of the earth. Yet in weight it is not so very much greater than the sun; for it is a huge ball of gas. The measurements indicated that this star is pulsating—now expanding, now contracting—in an unknown period and to an unknown extent.

For a long time nations have carefully guarded their standard yardstick or

Grimm's Fairy Tales or the *Arabian Nights*. Yet, in the case of light observed on the earth, it actually is true.

FitzGerald and Lorentz came forward with an explanation. To be sure, the explanation is as fantastic as the original observation, yet it is an explanation, and furthermore it is probably the truth.

If an object is flattened in the direction in which it is moving and if the amount of flattening depends upon the speed with which the body is moving, then that curious constancy of the velocity of light can be accounted for. When a body is moving 161,000 miles per second, it will be flattened to one-half its normal size. A ball would be flattened into a thick disc which would be one-half as thick as the original diameter of the ball; for it would be flattened both on its front surface and its rear

---

their standard meter; for it would be difficult, if not impossible, to accurately replace the unit if it were accidentally destroyed. Michelson measured the number of waves of a certain kind of light which are contained between the two ends of the standard meter at Paris; so that now this famous strip of platinum, which is kept in a vault of even temperature, can be replaced.

Michelson's most famous experiment was made in partnership with Morley. These two physicists showed that the velocity of light always is the same, whether it is measured in the direction in which the earth is moving or in the opposite direction. Upon the result of this experiment Einstein founded the special theory of relativity. The experiment recently was repeated at the Mt. Wilson Observatory under the direction of Michelson and in coöperation with other members of the staff. A new apparatus, a hundred times as accurate, was built. With this instrument the earlier observations of Michelson and Morley have been confirmed with the highest precision.

As director, A. A. Michelson made the physical laboratory of the University of Chicago the most famous in the Western hemisphere. Until his death he was research associate of Mt. Wilson Observatory of the Carnegie Institution of Washington. (Reproduced by permission of the University of Chicago Press. Courtesy of the Yerkes Observatory.)

173

surface. At least that is the way the ball would look to a spectator who thought that he was standing still.

If a yardstick were thrown through space at this enormous speed, it would immediately become only 18 inches long to that stationary observer. The moment it stopped it would become its normal length, if there is such a thing as "normal length." On the other hand, if the yardstick went through space sidewise, it would stay 36 inches long no matter how fast it went past the amazed but stationary observer; but it would become very thin as the speed increased. At the speed with which the earth goes around the sun, everything appears to be flattened or foreshortened by about one two hundred millionth ($\frac{1}{200,000,000}$) of its normal length and always, of course, in the direction in which the earth is moving.

Probably you are saying that this "FitzGerald contraction" cannot be true, for if it were, people surely would have discovered it long ago when they made accurate measurements in the laboratory. The joke is that the people in the laboratory —their eyes, hands, and measuring rods—are all being foreshortened in the same proportion. Therefore, they have been heretofore quite unaware of it, and only realized what was happening when they found that the velocity of light as measured on the earth was always constant.

No body, except an electron or proton, ever has been found

that moves as fast as 161,000 miles per second, and consequently no body is known to have been flattened or foreshortened to the extent of one-half its original length. The diameter of the earth as it moves around the sun is shortened two and one-half inches. Apparently nothing can move faster than the velocity of light —186,000 miles per second. As a body approaches this limiting speed it grows thinner and thinner to the man who thinks he is standing still, until it becomes a mere wafer when it approaches very closely to that maximum speed.

Perhaps you will study the reasons for this curious truth when you are in college, but in the meantime you can readily understand that any amount of flattening is possible when the body that is moving consists almost entirely of empty space. That a swarm of bees should change its shape is not surprising, and we have just discovered that a piece of iron is only a swarm of little atoms—little systems of electrons and protons.

The changes in length, weight and time, due to relative velocities, are the field of "Special Relativity." Einstein also developed a new theory of gravitation, "General Relativity," which for the first time connects gravity and light. He has been modest and has not been too sure that it is true. He has said substantially: "If it is true, then two minor but important consequences must be found to be true. These consequences are such as you can observe. If you do observe them and do find them to be as I have predicted, then you will be willing to believe that the great laws which I claim to have discovered are really part of this strange universe."

To realize this situation more vividly, imagine that you lived at the time of the Egyptian Pharaoh Akhnaton, about 1300 B.C. Let us suppose that you were one of those people who are said to be ahead of their time, just as the great Pharaoh Akhnaton now is known to have been, perhaps, a couple of thousand years ahead of his time. You had been making some good observations and you had the courage to speak freely about your discoveries. It had become increasingly clear to you that the earth is a round ball; yet you hesitated to say so because the Egyptians might think your reasons were foolish. Finally, when you did tell the people of the Nile Valley that the earth was round, you said: "If I am right, if this incredible idea is true, then several little minor things must also be true, and these little minor things you can observe for yourselves. If you find I am correct in these little minor things, then you will agree that my big idea that the earth is round probably also is true."

Then you would tell them how a boat ought to disappear over the horizon as it sailed out to sea. Your friends would go down to the mouth of the Nile River and watch a boat sail toward the island of Crete and they would say: "The appearance of that boat as it sails farther and farther away is just as you said it would be. Perhaps the earth is round as you claimed."

Also you would tell them that when the moon was next eclipsed, they would find that the great dark disc which was covering the moon was round, because it is the shadow of the round earth. When the next eclipse came, they would look very carefully and find that what you had predicted about a round shadow was true.

At last they would accept your idea that the earth is round, and then they would make some predictions on their own account. They might say: "Some day a sailor will take his boat entirely around this earth. He will leave the sea into which the Nile flows and sail far away into the great ocean. After hundreds of days he will return from the other side of the world."

In the next chapter we will describe some other curious things which are associated with Einstein's theories of both "Special Relativity" and "General Relativity."

XXVIII: EINSTEIN
AND SPACE AND TIME

ESIDES flattening, as a body goes through space, it also grows heavier. The flatter it gets the heavier it becomes. This is another statement, you will say, which ought to come from *Alice in Wonderland;* for when a body flattens due to speed, it doesn't become any wider—it simply grows thinner in the direction in which it is moving. Therefore, its volume becomes smaller and smaller until it is almost nothing as it nearly reaches 186,000 miles per second. Yet all this time it is growing heavier in proportion as it is growing thinner. Finally, just before it reaches 186,000 miles per second, it would have an inconceivably heavy weight.

Not only is this true, but it actually has been verified by direct observation, so that all strange things are not confined to fairy stories. Furthermore, some little high-speed bodies which increase their weight with their speed probably are very near you. They are in vacuum tubes in your radio set. Countless millions of little electrons dash across such a tube when the current is turned on. Under certain conditions, the speed of these electrons can be controlled and measured. They attain enormous speeds—scores of thousands of miles per second. Also it is possible to measure the weight of these electrons while they are dashing from one side of the tube to the other.

When these measurements of weight were made, it was found that that amazing story told by Einstein was true. The electron actually did gain weight with speed, and, what is still more remarkable, it gained just as much weight with each increase in speed as Einstein's formula required. Of course, the man in the laboratory thought he was standing still and so to him the electron's weight was increasing the faster it jumped from one side of the vacuum tube to the other. If he were riding on the electron, he wouldn't dream that he was gaining in weight with his increase of speed; for we don't realize that we are being distorted by the FitzGerald contraction as we madly revolve around the sun.

It would seem probable, therefore, that the FitzGerald contraction due to great speed also is true, and is a correct explanation of the constancy of the velocity of light as observed on the earth.

Einstein claimed that if his theory of General Relativity were true, the light from a star would be slightly bent when it passed very close to a large object like the sun. Also, he computed just how much it ought to be bent from its usual straight course. This was a very difficult prediction to verify; for the sun is so bright that ordinarily you cannot see the stars in the sky if they are near the sun. However, there are a few occasions when you can see even faint stars near the sun. Those occasions are when the blinding light of the sun is covered by the moon.

About once or twice a year, you remember, the moon comes so directly between us and the sun as to cover that luminary completely. The sun never is hidden in this way for more than 7 minutes and 40 seconds; but in those few minutes you can see the red flames of hydrogen gas, the brilliant corona, and the faint stars shining in the black sky close to the edge of the sun.

In 1919, at the total eclipse of the sun which was visible in Brazil, an English expedition photographed these stars, and then photographed them again some months later. If Einstein was correct, the two photographs would not be exactly alike. The photographs taken during the eclipse would be slightly distorted; for the light from the stars would be bent by the great mass of the sun. Of course, the sun won't stay very long in any one place in the sky. The earth, as you know, is running around it at the rate of 18 miles a second. So the people on the earth see the sun projected against the sky first in one place and then in another. It is like walking around a lamp which is in the center of a room. From one position you may see the lamp projected against the constellation of the Fireplace; from another as you walk around you see it in the direction of the constellation of the Bookcase. On Thanksgiving Day the earth is so placed that we always see the sun projected against the constellation of the Scorpion (Figure 15). By Christmas, however, the earth has moved so far that the sun is seen in the direction of Sagittarius (Figure 15). Therefore, if you wait a few months after an eclipse, the sun will apparently move away to another part of the sky and allow you to photograph the stars in their normal positions, undisturbed by the distorting effect of our own great star.

Again Einstein's prediction was verified, and it was confirmed during the total eclipse in 1922, by astronomers from Australia, Canada, and the United States. In 1922, the confirmation was remarkable. Not only were the stars displaced from their normal positions, but they were found to be displaced by the exact amount which Einstein had claimed they should be. This verification was especially true in the work done by Lick Observatory under the direction of William Wallace Campbell, who was in charge of the Lick Observatory's expedition to Australia.

The next proof that Einstein is correct also was given by the sun. In accordance with the General Theory of Relativity, the tremendous power of gravity on the sun makes the electrons dance around the protons a very little less rapidly than they would if they were dancing and radiating light on this earth. The activity of the electron-proton system which forms an atom

181

is slowed down. On the sun, the tremendous power of that thing called gravity acts on those queer electrons like a dense fog, or as if the electrons had been immersed in water. As a result of this slowing down of the activity of electrons, the light waves are sent out at slightly longer intervals. To our eyes, if they were very, very delicate, that would mean that the light from the sun is a little more red than as if those same atoms were vibrating on a smaller body like the earth. On a smaller body, of course, the power of gravity would not be so great, and therefore it would not act so strongly as a brake on the vibrations of the electrons.

Of course, no human eye ever could distinguish so small a variation in color as this. However, this effect can be measured, for when the light becomes ever so little redder, the dark lines in the spectrum are moved toward the red. In this particular case the movement is extremely slight, so that under ordinary conditions it would have been hopeless to try to detect it. But at the Mt. Wilson Observatory of the Carnegie Institution of Washington, where the atmospheric conditions are excellent and the instruments the most powerful in the world, St. John was able to detect and measure this exceedingly slight displacement in the lines.[1]

This curious effect of gravitation on the activity of an atom

[1] *Evidence for the Gravitational Displacement of the Lines in the Solar Spectrum Predicted by Einstein's Theory.* Contributions from Mt. Wilson Observatory, No. 348, by Charles E. St. John.

is called the Red Shift. In the future, Sam and his friends may often read of new discoveries about the Red Shift, not only in connection with the sun, but with some star, and even with very distant star clusters, or spiral nebulae. It was shortly after St. John's determination of the Red Shift in the solar spectrum that Walter S. Adams of the Mt. Wilson Observatory made an exceedingly interesting study of the Red Shift on a very faint star, closely associated with the very bright star Sirius.

For thousands of years Sirius, called the Dog Star, was worshiped by our ancestors. They used to build their temples sometimes so that if you stood at the altar and looked down the corridor and through the main door, you would see Sirius as it rose from the eastern horizon. This sun, much like our sun but at an enormous distance—this brilliant star α (Alpha), Canis Majoris—was supposed not only to affect the happiness of men and women, but even the weather. Hence, temples were built for the worship of this Dog Star in order to make it kindly disposed to the builders and owners of the temple. Even now you often will hear about the "dog days," the foggy and sultry days in summer which, on the North Atlantic coast at least, commence about the time Sirius first appears in the dawn just before sunrise.

Those great ruins called Stonehenge in England are all that remain of some prehistoric temple which was built about 3,000

183

years ago. Perhaps this temple was used for the worship of Sirius, as well as the sun.

Now we neither worship Sirius, nor are we afraid of it. We know that it has nothing to do with our happiness or with the weather. However, we find it extremely interesting because it has a most remarkable companion.

A celestial P. T. Barnum who owned a heavenly circus, would have placed the companion of Sirius in a side show as one of the heaviest stars for its size in captivity. It would be a sight worth seeing, too; for the companion of Sirius is made of such solid stuff that a pint of it would weigh more than 20 tons here on this earth.

In 1850, the Russian astronomer Bessel found that Sirius was moving among the stars in a wobbly path. Instead of going in a straight line as a respectable star should do, it was sometimes on one side and sometimes on the other side of a straight line. Bessel felt convinced that it was due to the potent influence of some invisible companion.

When two people hold hands and whirl around each other on the ice, if they are about the same weight, they both will revolve around a point which is midway between them. On the other hand, if one fellow is very much larger than the other, the little fellow will swing around the big fellow. In all cases, however, each swings around a point between them and, literally speaking, not around each other.

184

In the same way the earth and moon revolve around a common "center of gravity" in a period of not quite one month. The earth is so much heavier than the moon that the center of gravity is only about 3,000 miles from the center of the earth, or about 1,000 miles below the surface. The true path of the earth is described by this imaginary center of gravity. That salamander would see the earth wobbling first on one side and then on the other side of the true path, but never getting more than about 3,000 miles to one side or the other. Even if the salamander couldn't see the moon, he would know about where it ought to be because of this irregularity in the earth's motion. So Bessel knew that Sirius must have a companion which was causing all this trouble. It must be a faint companion, for although Bessel had a good telescope, he could not see any star at all near Sirius. If it is so faint a star as that and yet powerful enough to pull that very bright star Sirius out of its straight path, it must be very heavy for its size; that is, it must contain a great deal of substance in a small space; for a star's power to influence other stars by gravitation depends very largely upon the number of atoms it contains. It would be more accurate to say it depends upon the number of protons the star contains. If a small and faint star possesses a great deal of real substance, that is, a vast number of protons, packed close together its effect will be correspondingly powerful. Therefore, the companion of Sirius must be tremendously heavy for its size.

Twelve years later, in 1862, Alvin Clarke, the famous telescope maker at Cambridge, Massachusetts, was testing a large telescope by looking at Sirius. Then for the first time the companion was seen and, furthermore, seen in the place it ought to occupy to account for the wobbly motion of Sirius. For by means of the law of gravity the position of this faint and unseen star had been carefully computed from year to year. Astronomers knew where the star was at all times even if they could not see it. The discovery of this star in the place predicted was one of the historical and somewhat sensational tests of Sir Isaac Newton's law of gravity. Now Sirius has been asked again to help confirm another great law of the universe— the Red Shift.

As you may remember, the movement of the dark lines in the spectrum also can be caused by the rapid recession of the object which is giving the light. The waves are dropped by the retreating object at longer intervals than when the bright object is standing still. To have two very different things both cause the Red Shift in the lines of the spectrum is very confusing. It sometimes is possible for the Red Shift to be made by both causes working together. A very heavy body giving rise to tremendous gravitation might also be running away from you as fast as it can. Then gravitation would slow down the activity of the atoms so as to make the dark lines in the spectrum move a little toward the red. Also the rapid speed away from you would make fewer waves of light enter your eye per second, and therefore cause the dark lines in the spectrum to move a little toward the red.

Sirius at this point comes to our rescue. Thanks to Bessel, Clarke, and others, the velocities of Sirius and its companion are well known. Also, the companion is known to be very heavy for its size. This is a good thing, as such a great number of protons packed into a small space produces a tremendous force of gravity at the star's surface. Therefore, the companion of Sirius was chosen by W. S. Adams of Mt. Wilson Observatory, to verify this other feature of Einstein's theory. Again Einstein was shown to be correct. The observed shift in the lines corresponded with the computed value.

So far, all the efforts to verify Einstein's theory have been entirely successful. Therefore, it is at least probable that the theory as a whole is correct. If this is so, then we have discovered some interesting and strange features of this universe in which we live.

Time, for one thing, is found to be fickle. It always has been considered to be the majestic measure of progress through all the ages. Of course, no one has ever known what time is, and no one now knows anything about its real nature. However, in connection with the "Special Theory of Relativity," time is found to be seriously affected by velocity. Each man, to a certain extent, has his own standard of time. From such a man's point of view every other man's timepiece is either too fast or too slow. In *Space, Time, and Gravitation* (Cambridge

EINSTEIN AND SPACE AND TIME

University Press), by E. S. Eddington, there can be found an excellent description of this curious feature of time. Eddington says that it always has been a favorite dream to imagine a magic carpet on which one could fly to the remote parts of space with the speed of light. The dreamers took care to store the carpet with ample food to last the traveler for centuries, for the story-teller realized well the enormous distances over which this magic carpet would be obliged to fly with the speed of a sunbeam. Then Mr. Eddington points out that since the dreamer was traveling with the speed of light, time, for him, would cease to exist. He would arrive at his destination no more aged than when he left. Since the journey, so far as the traveler was concerned, would last but an instant, he would have no time to eat. If, without stopping, the dreamer returned to the earth on his magic carpet with sunlight speed, he would find his country many centuries older, while he would be as youthful as the day he left.

This is something we cannot comprehend. We only know that time, like weight and thickness, is seriously influenced by velocity and gravitation. Also, so far no method has been found by which such queer variations in time can be verified by direct observation. All we can say is that this incredible characteristic of time is probably true, for we have always been successful whenever we have been able to verify by observation certain features of Einstein's theory.

ONE OF THE OLDEST OBSERVATORIES IN AMERICA

Figure 105. The Astronomical Observatory of Harvard College, Cambridge, Massachusetts. (Courtesy of the Harvard College Observatory.)

THE GREAT HOOKER TELESCOPE

Figure 106. More than 8 feet in diameter (100 inches), this telescope has been the camera which has made many of the beautiful photographs of nebulae. It has assisted astronomers to add materially to our knowledge of the universe. (From a photograph taken at the Mt. Wilson Observatory. Courtesy of the Mt. Wilson Observatory.)

TENTATIVE DESIGN FOR THE 200-INCH TELESCOPE

Figure 107. When this giant telescope 16 feet in diameter is completed, our knowledge of the world will be still further increased. This telescope will pick up and make visible on the photographic plate faint light which left some island universe several hundred million years ago.

"To the astronomical and physical researches of Galileo we are chiefly indebted for our escape from the magic and superstition of the past. But we owe him a larger debt. His telescope, followed by others of increasing power, pushed back the hampering boundaries of the universe and step by step advanced into larger and larger spheres, where the same laws are found to reign, unbroken by distance or by time. Thus arose a new and vast conception of an ordered cosmos, stretching away to the countless 'island universes' beyond our own galactic island, in which the solar system is as a grain of sand." (From *Building the 200-inch Telescope*, by Geo. E. Hale, chairman of the Observatory Council of the California Institute of Technology. Published in *Harper's Magazine*, November, 1929. Courtesy of the Astrophysical Observatory of the California Institute of Technology.)

A MOUNTAIN OBSERVATORY IN PERU

Figure 108. From photographs taken in this mountain observatory the law of the Cepheid variable stars was discovered. (A photograph of the Harvard College branch observatory at Arequipa, Peru. Courtesy of the Harvard College Observatory.)

XXIX: RESEARCH

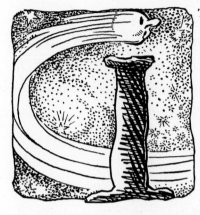 T WAS only a few centuries ago that our ancestors thought the earth and even the stars were only a few thousand years old. The world was very small and cozy and each star might reasonably be supposed to be acquainted with every other star. Then Galileo broke a hole in that medieval wall of prejudice and superstition by means of his telescope. Human beings began to realize the vast extent of the world. Gradually they learned that the world was as old as it was large. We have explored as far back in time as we have in distant space, and the end is not yet in sight.

We have been sailing down the river of knowledge. We do not know its source and we do not even know at which point we embarked. If any one ever has reached the mouth, he has not returned to tell us of the great ocean which may lie beyond. During the last few thousand years, perhaps the keenest intellectual pleasure of certain human beings has been to explore the banks of the stream and to study the teeming life of the river. Yet there was a time, not far back in the river's

189

life, when, as ape-men, we were not interested in the grandeur of the distant scenery, the amazing mechanism of our own bodies, and the mystery of our existence. There may come a time in the distant future when again we will cease to be interested in the events of this interminable voyage. When such a time comes, we will have run our course either because of exhaustion, or perhaps because some cosmic cloud has made the earth either intensely cold or insufferably hot.